A **DYNAMO GURU**™ Journey fro
Consultant To Thriving Info

SYSTEMIZING FROM GURU TO DYNAMO GURO™

GINA ST. GEORGE

BEYOND
PUBLISHING INC

New York | Los Angeles | London | Sydney

ISBN Hardcover: 978-1-63792-985-8
ISBN Softcover: 978-1-63792-640-6

DEDICATION

This book is dedicated to Andy Sokol, the biggest dynamo I've ever known. I'm a better person for having known you.

ACKNOWLEDGEMENTS

I would like to thank Craig Duswalt, my friend and mentor who never quit insisting that everyone needs to have a book to market their expertise and stand out from the crowd. Because of you, I now have a series complete. To Tim Gillette, who has always reminded me to keep things simple, thank you for reminding me that it's all possible. To Michael Butler and the team at Beyond Publishing, many thanks for all of the support and encouragement to complete this project. I have to thank Andrei Mincov and the Trademark Factory, without whom I wouldn't have found my trademarked brand that would lead me forward. To Audrey and Michael, thanks for holding down the fort and running operations so well that I had the freedom to work on my books and programs. To Katie, thank you for doing too many things for me to list and for always being there for me. Last, but not least, thank you to Marty for being my companion and for quietly being in my corner, letting me be me as I work on my projects.

TABLE OF CONTENTS

PREFACE

I lace up my running shoes and head out for a jog around the neighborhood, the rhythmic pounding of my footsteps on the pavement a soothing cadence. The fresh air fills my lungs, and the gentle breeze brushes against my skin, creating a sense of freedom and release. As I round a corner, lost in my thoughts, someone calls out my name.

"Hey, aren't you Christine Casey?" a friendly voice interrupts my reverie. I slow down, slightly surprised, and turn to face the source of the voice. A woman stands there, a warm smile on her face, her eyes holding a glimmer of recognition.

I pause, a bit taken aback that someone in the neighborhood recognizes me as the owner of WellQuest.

Wow, I think, *I guess my business is becoming bigger than I realized.*

I smile as I share, "You know, I'm not just Christine Turner anymore. I'm now Christine Turner Casey. Got married not too long ago."

She nods with genuine interest, encouraging me to continue. "Wow, congratulations! So, tell me, Christine Casey, how did you end up where you are now?"

I chuckle at her curiosity and dive into my journey. "Well, it's been quite a ride. Back when I was Christine Casey, I used to struggle to find customers for my wellness business, Serene Solutions. It was tough, and making ends meet was a constant challenge. At the time, I had this notion that Ethan, my now-husband, was a bit of a jerk. Funny how perspectives change, huh?"

She laughs along, and I continue sharing my story. "And oh, my mom, she wasn't on board with my business dreams either. She had her reservations, wanted me to go a different route. But with the support of friends like Lily, I kept pushing forward. We even tried an open house event that didn't exactly go as planned, but we didn't let that discourage us."

I take a breath, reflecting on the journey. "Then came a turning point. I attended a marketing seminar that opened my eyes to new possibilities. And you won't believe this, but fate has its ways – I ran into Ethan on the plane back home from that seminar. We got talking, and I learned more in those few hours than I had in months."

As we walk along, I recall the pivotal moments. "With the help of Lily, Alex, and Ethan, we started creating reels, putting out content that resonated with people. Slowly but surely,

things started to take off. And then came the collaboration project with Ava Summers, the famous personality. It was like a dream come true."

I glance at her, a mix of nostalgia and pride in my voice. "It's been a journey of ups and downs, but each step has brought me to this point – Christine Casey, now Christine Casey Turner. And now, my business has transformed into WellQuest, a hub of wellness and balance."

She listens intently, and I can see the inspiration in her eyes. "It's incredible how far you've come," she says, genuine admiration in her voice.

I smile, grateful for this unexpected connection. "Thank you. And just remember, whatever you're dreaming of, whatever hurdles you're facing, there's always a way forward. It's all about determination, support, and never giving up."

As we continue our walk, I realize that this conversation isn't just about sharing my story, it's about passing on the torch of encouragement and empowerment, one person's journey inspiring another's.

CHAPTER 1

OVERWHELMED AND OVERCOMMITTED

"No, no!" I hiss at the phone as it rings, yet again.

I drop my pencil onto the sketch I've been working on. It lands on a figure I've drawn of a figure engaged in a yoga pose, the central design of the latest poster that Dr. Martinez from Brownsville Medical Clinic has commissioned me for.

The phone rings again, and I groan. Before turning to pick it up, I allow myself one last glance at the project. Surrounding the central image are depictions of fresh produce, open books, and active lifestyle elements that underscore the pillars of wellness. I've added thoughtfully placed phrases like "Nurture Your Body and Mind" and "Embrace Wellness Every Day" resonate as gentle reminders.

"I was almost done," I grumble as I move toward the phone. But, it's too late. It stops. I feel slightly relieved about this, it's one less thing to worry about. But, when I glance around my home office, my mind feels no more relaxed.

The desk in front of me is a battlefield of papers, notebooks, and half-filled coffee cups. Stacks of documents teeter precariously, threatening to cascade to the floor at any moment. The walls are adorned with scribbled notes and colorful mind maps, visual evidence of my ongoing efforts to manage the overwhelming avalanche of responsibilities.

In one chaotic corner, there's a jumble of notes and materials sprawled out for the impending speech at Brownsville Elementary, an event that's practically breathing down my neck. The weight of molding young minds with my words hangs over me like a heavy, suffocating fog, it's both exhilarating and suffocating, all at once.

And then, on the other side of this maddening chaos, there's the half-finished presentation for the local law firm glaring back at me from the mocking computer screen. The relentless ticking of the clock is like a relentless reminder, each second ticking away my dwindling sanity as I scramble to string together sentences that'll somehow captivate my audience, or at least keep them from falling asleep.

As if that weren't enough, there's this whole other beast, those personalized fitness plans, my latest venture entwined with the Flex and Flourish Gym. Every single one is like a tiny, intricate puzzle piece, painstakingly tailored to meet the aspirations of different individuals. I've been pouring over every agonizing detail, dissecting every workout, every damn instruction, in a desperate attempt to ensure they're a perfect match for their goals.

It's like I'm trapped in a whirlwind of chaos and ambition, struggling to keep my head above water as these relentless demands threaten to pull me under. Every corner of this room feels like a battlefield, and I'm just a soldier frantically trying to hold it all together.

I tangle my fingers through my hair and pull. *How will I ever get all of this done? Ring!*

I swing my head around to see my phone beginning to ring again, its insistence mingling with the rhythmic ticking of the clock. The sight of it feels like a volcano exploding in my mind.

I let out a whimper before my eyes land on the circular mirror hanging on the far wall. It is partially covered with Post-it notes, but through them, I catch a glimpse of myself. My dark hair is sticking out every which way, frizzed out from the number of times I've pulled at it with stress. There are dark circles under my eyes from nights filled with restless sleep. My eyes look almost hollow, unfocused with the amount of tasks hanging over my head.

I steal a fleeting glance at the phone, its call now accompanied by a buzz of urgency. I pick it up reluctantly.

"Hello, this is Christine with WellQuest. How can we help you on your journey today?" I say into the receiver, my voice tinged with fake cheerfulness.

"Christine! Hey, it's Lily," the chipper voice cuts through the phone.

My heart warms at the sound of my best friend's voice, but it does not cut through the weight of my other hanging responsibilities.

"Lil, hey, it's great to hear from you," I say. My eyes dart around the room, realizing that I don't have time for this. "Look, can I call you back later? I have a ton of work to do."

There is a pause on the other line, and then Lily finally responds, "Sure thing. Hey, let me know if there is anything I can do to help-"

I cut her off. "It's okay, Lil, I just have a lot on my plate," I say.

I don't want to involve Lily and Alex in the business again. They had done so much for me as I started off, really putting a lot at stake to help me get to where I am now. The last thing I want to do is butt into their happy marriage. On top of that, my best friend is now pregnant.

Pregnant, I think. *I can still hardly believe it.*

There is no way I can ask her to help me, not again, not now.

"I'll call you back later, okay?" I reassure her. "I promise."

I hang up the phone. Gritting my teeth, I turn back to the almost-finished poster for the doctor's office. But, now that I've become distracted, I can't prevent the thoughts of all of my other daunting tasks ahead. The law firm, the elementary school, the gym, they're all waiting on me to deliver. On top of that, I still need to film videos for my Instagram feed.

How will I do all of this on time? How? I wonder.

I realize I'm teetering on the edge of overwhelming stress, so I decide to give meditation a shot, hoping it might offer me some relief.

Practice what you preach, I tell myself.

I walk over to the corner of the room, where a purple yoga mat rests in its rolled-up form. I lay it out among the scattered books and papers on the floor and then sit down, willing myself to relax.

I close my eyes and try to let go, to find that inner calm I so desperately need. But it's like my mind has a mind of its own, it's a chaotic swirl of thoughts, each one a nagging reminder of the tasks that are piling up around me. Despite my best efforts, I can't seem to break free from this mental loop. It's as if the more I try not to think about my to-do list, the more those very tasks assert their presence, refusing to be ignored.

Frustration bubbles up, and my attempt at meditation becomes this frustrating dance between seeking serenity and grappling with the relentless demands that refuse to fade into the background.

Suddenly, the quiet of my attempted meditation is interrupted by the loud, unmistakable cries of my young daughter. There is a knock at the door.

I moan to myself before calling out, "Yes?"

Ethan steps into the room, his blonde hair falling over his eyes and his usually well-trimmed beard now overgrown. A surge of love flows through my body at the sight of my husband. But then it's overpowered by the sight of him cradling our thirteen-month-old Emmy in his arms, her cries filling the air. Life with a fussy baby is tense, and it's difficult to focus on the affection we used to have for each other.

"Hey, Chris, I need to pop out and check on the gym for a bit. Could you watch her?" he asks, weariness tinging his voice.

I glance around at my sea of tasks, my stress levels already through the roof. The combination of Emmy's cries and Ethan's request feels like a tidal wave crashing into my already cluttered mind.

"Ethan, I really don't have time right now," I respond, my voice sharper than I intended.

His eyebrows furrow, his expression a mix of concern and frustration. "I know you're busy, but I just need to sort a few things. Can you manage for a bit?"

I feel my patience slipping, the mounting pressure squeezing my ability to respond calmly. "Can't you call my mom? She's just a phone call away," I retort, my tone laced with exasperation.

Ethan's gaze narrows, hurt flickering in his eyes before he nods. "Fine, I'll call her," he replies, his voice edged with resignation.

He turns to leave, Emmy's cries growing louder as he walks away, leaving me with a pang of guilt but an overwhelming urge to focus on the never-ending tasks in front of me. As he heads out the door, I stand up from the yoga mat and force my attention back to my work, determined not to let my stress devour me, even though a part of me wonders if I might have been too harsh.

...

Hours pass.

The work doesn't get any easier.

I feel like I haven't made a dent.

But, after what feels like an eternity of typing and clicking, I reach a point where I can take a breath.

I push my chair back and stretch, feeling the knots in my shoulders loosen just a bit. With a sigh of relief, I step out of my cluttered office, the air of the living room feeling strangely fresh against my skin.

And there, on the carpeted floor, a heartwarming scene unfolds before me. My mother sits on the carpet, a bright smile on her face. Her ashore blonde hair is clipped back and she has replaced her usual rigid attire with a relaxed sweatshirt.

She's taking turns stacking blocks with Emmy. My young daughter's light tufts of hair glow in the dim light as she carefully lifts a pink cube and places it atop a blue one. She claps her hands animatedly when it stays balanced in lace.

My mother's voice is a gentle melody as she exclaims, "Look, Emmy, you did it! You stacked the blocks all by yourself!"

Emmy's face lights up with a triumphant grin, her chubby hands clutching onto the tower of blocks she managed to assemble. The sense of accomplishment radiates from her, and for a moment, I'm filled with a surge of pride.

But as quickly as the joy washes over me, a pang of bitterness follows. I watch the scene before me, the warmth of the moment contrasting sharply with the cold realization that I wasn't here to witness this milestone firsthand. Guilt and regret swirl in my chest, their weight is heavy and suffocating.

"I'm so proud of you, sweetie," my mother coos, her eyes shining with adoration as she showers Emmy with praise.

I force a smile, my heart aching as I join them on the floor. "You're amazing, Emmy," I add, my voice tinged with a mix of genuine pride and a tinge of longing.

My mother looks up at me, her gaze filled with understanding. "She's growing so fast, Christine. It's these little moments that make it all worthwhile, right?"

I nod, my smile faltering slightly as I wrestle with the conflicting emotions inside me. I know my mother didn't mean it, but her words seem to mock me.

"I'm so glad that you have to work, I love getting my little granddaughter all to myself!" she adds.

I bite my lip as a surge of bitterness rushes through my body. I know that my mother didn't intend to hurt me, but her words cut deep.

I'm grateful for my mother's presence in Emmy's life. I am. But still, a part of me yearns to be there for every single one of these milestones, to share in the small victories that shape Emmy's world.

Just as I'm starting to soak in the moment, I hear a sharp *ping*.

The notifications from my phone jolts me back to reality. I pull my phone from my pocket and see that the screen is flashing with a reminder, that it's time for me to go live on Instagram.

Sighing, I tear my gaze away from my mother and Emmy, a twinge of reluctance tugging at my heart. With a heavy but determined stride, I turn back toward my office, leaving behind a scene of precious connection to step into the world of demands.

Reflections

How do the elements of this chapter relate to your business?

Actions to Take

1 _____

2 _____

3 _____

CHAPTER 2

WHEN LIFE GIVES YOU ORANGES

The kitchen bustles with activity as I move swiftly between the stove and the counter, a symphony of clinking utensils and sizzling ingredients filling the air. Emmy's highchair occupies a corner of the room, her big eyes observing my every move with curiosity.

Ethan leans against the counter, a gentle smile on his face. "Need any help?" he offers.

I glance at him, my thoughts already swirling in the whirlwind of recipes and deadlines that dominate my mind. "Thanks, but I've got this under control," I reply hurriedly, my words almost running into each other as my focus remains firmly on the pot before me

Ethan's eyebrows furrow, concern etching lines on his forehead. "So," he begins, his voice tentative. "We haven't really had a chance to talk today. How was your day?" His words are gentle, an invitation to share a moment beyond the rush

Caught in my culinary frenzy, his question barely registers. My mental checklist seems to drown out everything else as I continue to stir the simmering sauce.

"It was busy," I murmur absentmindedly, my voice hardly lifting from the task at hand. I see a flicker of emotion play across my husband's face, but I dismiss it.

I'll catch up with him when I finish my work, I think to myself as I fill three plates with food.

I place the plates around the table and we sit down, Emmy's highchair positioned at one end. Her delighted babbles fill the room with an infectious charm as Ethan and I scootch in our chairs. I sigh, ready to take a short break from all of the stress of the day. I cut off a piece of chicken and chew it slowly, letting the taste seep through my senses.

With a sigh, I look up at Ethan, who now has a distant gaze in his eyes.

"What did you do today?" I ask, now ready to start a conversation.

But his response is a far cry from the usual reciprocity. He stares at his plate, his features a mix of contemplation and something else, a subdued sadness. I shrug, sure that it is nothing to worry about. The clinking of utensils and the occasional burst of Emmy's laughter form a backdrop to this meal, yet an unspoken tension lingers like a veil over the table.

I take another bite of the food, the flavors registering in my mouth without leaving a lasting impression. My mind, however, is in another realm entirely, a realm of emails, deadlines, and unfinished projects that scream for my attention even in this fleeting moment of togetherness. My responses to Emmy's joyful babbles are automatic, a mechanical reflex while my thoughts race elsewhere.

With a sigh, I push back from the table, my chair scraping against the floor as I rise. The remnants of our quiet meal stare back at me from the plates, a lingering reminder of the fleeting moment of togetherness. As Ethan scoops up Emmy, their laughter echoing through the air, I hastily gather the dishes, my hands working in a blur as I rinse and stack them. The water's warmth seeps through the soap-sud-covered gloves, the repetitive motions soothing my restless mind.

Ethan's voice drifts in from the bathroom, where he has started to give her a bath. Emmy's bubbly giggles intertwined with his words. I catch snippets of their conversation, my heart tugging at the harmonious connection they share. It's a sound that should bring me comfort, but a nagging sensation in the back of my mind keeps me tethered to my work.

With the dishes finally put away, I make my way back to my office, each step a reluctant surrender to the demands that have come to define my life. The glow of my computer screen beckons, and I settle into the familiar rhythm of typing. The speech for Brownsville Elementary demands my attention, it's looming deadline is an unignorable weight on my shoulders.

I read through my notes, the words dancing before me as I search for the perfect way to engage young minds.

The minutes tick by.

As I craft sentences and weave anecdotes, my mind briefly flits to the scene in the other room. Ethan's soothing lullabies and Emmy's contented coos intermingle with the clicking of keys beneath my fingers. Guilt nags at my conscience, but I push it aside, my focus narrowing to the words on the screen.

Hours slip away.

The moon's gentle glow filters through the window and acts as a reminder of the passage of time. The speech has begun to take form, but there is still a good amount of work to get done. The soft hum of the computer fills the room as my fingers dance across the keyboard, words and ideas flowing seamlessly from my mind to the screen. The task at hand demands my full attention, each sentence a puzzle piece that I meticulously arrange. The screen's glow casts

a dim light, the room's atmosphere a reflection of the intensity that has become my constant companion.

The creak of the door draws my attention, and I glance up to find Ethan standing there, his eyes weary and his face etched with concern. He takes a step closer, his arms outstretched in an embrace meant to provide comfort.

He's so sweet, I think, *but I don't have time for this.*

Instinctively, I raise my hand, palm outward, a silent plea for him to halt.

"I'm in the middle of something, Ethan," I murmur, my tone distracted as I return my gaze to the screen. My focus is unyielding, the work's hold on me unrelenting.

He hesitates, his arms slowly retreating, and I sense his disappointment even before he speaks. "Christine, you've been like this for days now. Always busy, always absorbed in your work," he says, his voice tinged with a mix of frustration and hurt.

My shoulders tense, a twinge of guilt flickering within me, but I push it aside, my attention resolutely fixed on the task before me. "I have deadlines to meet, Ethan. You know how important this is."

His sigh is heavy, a weight that settles between us. "I understand the importance of your work, Christine, but it feels like you're slipping away. You're here, but you're not really present."

The accusation stings, and for a moment, I wrestle with a surge of emotion. But I push it down, burying it beneath layers of determination and obligation. "I'm just trying to make everything work," I retort, my voice more defensive than I intended.

Ethan's eyes search mine, a mix of sadness and frustration dancing in their depths. "But at what cost, Christine? You used to have time for us, for Emmy. Now it's like we're secondary."

My fingers grip the edge of the keyboard, my jaw clenched as I hold back the torrent of words that threatens to spill forth. I want to explain, to make him understand the weight that rests on my shoulders, but the words remain lodged in my throat.

Ethan sighs and puts one hand gently on my shoulder. "Look, I know that you are stressed. I don't mean to pressure you, either," he says with a gentle tone. "Can you at least go pick up some milk for us? We're all out and Emmy is going to need some more."

I glance back at my work, and my instincts tell me to deny his request.

I have so much to do, I think, *how could I possibly go to the store right now?*

But then I look over at Ethan. When our eyes meet, I see compassion that reaches far beyond the surface, carrying with it an undeniable undercurrent of genuine hurt. My heart aches for him, and I know that I have to do as he asks.

I force a smile. "Okay," I tell him. "Fair enough."

...

I step through the sliding glass doors of the grocery store, the artificial chill of the air conditioning washing over me. The overhead lights cast a stark glow on the aisles, and the familiar hum of chatter and rustling shopping bags surround me. Despite the bustling scene, a heavy knot of distress lingers within me, a constant reminder of the mounting workload waiting for my attention.

Okay, I tell myself, *just get the milk and go home.*

I turn down the produce aisle, hoping to make a shortcut to the refrigerated dairy at the back of the store. I walk quickly, not wanting to waste a moment of time. As I move, a stray hair falls in front of my eyes. I reach up to push it back behind my ear but, when I do, my elbow collides with an orange.

The force of my elbow sends the orange flying across the aisle. I watch as it bounces one, two, three times before coming to a halt.

No big deal, I think.

But then, suddenly, the rest of the oranges on the shelf come toppling down. Suddenly, it's a fruity avalanche, and I'm caught in the middle of this unexpected chaos. Oranges drop and bounce all around my feet, causing a commotion so loud that the few other shoppers in the area turn and raise their eyebrows.

Great, I think, *just great.*

With a muttered half-grumble, half-mumble, I can't help but vent my frustration to no one in particular.

"Of course, this happens now," I mutter to myself. "I've got a mountain of work waiting, and here I am playing fruit pick-up."

As I gingerly gather the wayward oranges, my thoughts are a swirl of to-do lists, deadlines, and impending tasks that stubbornly cling to my mind. It's like a mental carousel of

responsibilities, spinning faster and faster with each piece of citrus I retrieve. Inwardly, I'm urging myself to hurry, to get this done and move on, my internal monologue a chorus of time constraints and obligations.

I reach for another orange, but a slightly wrinkled hand falls upon it before mine does. Surprised, I look up to see a woman with long, sleek white hair standing above me.

"It looks like you are a little flustered," the woman says. "Can I help you?"

I shake my head, gathering up a few more oranges. "It's okay, really," I tell the woman. "It's my fault that it happened."

The woman grins before bending over to pick up a second orange. "You know, I make a living out of helping others find ways out of stress," she says in a soothing voice as she places the oranges back on the shelf. "There is no shame in asking others for help. You know, even if you feel like asking others would hurt your chances of success, it can sometimes be what makes you even more fortunate."

My hand closes around another orange as I ponder her words. *Even if you feel like asking others would hurt your chances of success,* she had said. Somehow, those words strike home. *Is that what I've been afraid of?* I wonder.

I think back to how, earlier today, I had been juggling so many tasks. Trying to create those posters for the doctor's office, the speech for the elementary school, the presentation for the law firm- it was all so overwhelming, yet even when Lily offered me help, I'd denied it.

Am I afraid of asking for help? I wonder.

I turn to face the woman and watch with awe as she picks up the last orange. I can't help but notice that she is wearing a well-tailored business suit that perfectly compliments her figure. Her makeup is neatly done and a Dolce and Gabbana handbag hangs over one shoulder. When she straightens herself up and holds one orange in the air, she looks like the epitome of a woman who has her life together.

What is her secret? I think.

As if to answer my question, the woman smiles. "I mean it," she begins. "Sometimes, a little help isn't a bad thing." She reaches a hand in my direction. "I'm Chloe Miller, business consultant. It's nice to meet you."

I shake her hand and introduce myself, "Christine Turner," I say.

Chloe's expression becomes earnest, her eyes locking onto mine. "Christine, I couldn't help but overhear your little mutterings earlier. The ones about a mountain of work and time slipping away."

I'm taken aback for a moment, surprised by her insight. "Oh, well, you know how it is. Life gets crazy sometimes."

Chloe nods, her expression empathetic. "Absolutely. But here's the thing, Christine. It doesn't have to be that way. I specialize in helping businesses like yours find a smoother path, one where you're not constantly juggling everything on your own."

I raise an eyebrow, intrigued despite myself. "Really? How do you do that?"

Her smile widens, genuine enthusiasm radiating from her. "WellQuest, right? I've been hearing a lot about it on social media. You've really created quite a storm!"

I smile, pride washing through my body despite my lingering stresses. "Thank you," I say. It's not the first time I've been recognized by a stranger, but the notion still comes as a shock.

"How about we chat sometime?" Chloe says. "I'd love to learn more about your vision, and your goals, and see if there's a way to eliminate some of those unnecessary stresses that come along with running a business."

Her offer sounds nice. It's tempting, for sure. But, would I really want to spend money on a consultant, when everything is running fine?

It's fine, it really is, I tell myself. *I can do this on my own.*

But, I smile politely anyway. "That would be nice," I tell Chloe, putting on a polite face for the grocery store environment. "Thank you."

Chloe reaches into that Dolce and Gabbana handbag and pulls out a small piece of paper. When she hands it to me, I'm surprised by how sturdy it is. I can tell that it is made of quality materials. In embossed teal lettering are the words, *Chloe Miller, Business Consulting*, followed by a phone number.

I nod politely to Chloe before turning back in the direction of the dairy aisle. As I walk toward the milk, I turn the card over in my hands, surprised to see that there is more writing on the back.

It reads, *Let me help you reshape your dreams.*

Reflections

How do the elements of this chapter relate to your business?

Actions to Take

1 _____

2 _____

3 _____

CHAPTER 3

DONUT YOU WANT TO CHANGE

I step into the house, the familiar scent of my favorite lavender candles enveloping me as I close the door behind me. The silence that greets me is a stark contrast to the hustle and bustle of the grocery store, and I move quietly as I navigate the dimly lit rooms. The house seems to hold its breath, as if aware of the weight that rests on my shoulders.

In the kitchen, I place the milk in the fridge, the soft hum of its interior a soothing contrast to the cacophony of thoughts swirling within my mind. Chloe's words echo in my ears, her offer of help lingering like a gentle whisper. A part of me, a small and cautious part, considers the idea, the notion that someone else could share the load, could guide me through the labyrinth of challenges.

But then, like a reflex, my mind races to dismiss the thought. I shake my head slightly, my doubts finding a voice in the shadows.

"I can manage this," I mutter under my breath, my voice resolute. "I've handled tough situations before, and I'll handle this too."

The idea of seeking outside help clashes with independence that has been my guiding force for as long as I can remember. Sure, my friends came to my aid as I took WellQuest off the ground. For that, I will always be thankful. But now, recently, I've prided myself on being self-reliant, on finding solutions to problems on my own. The notion of investing money into a consultant feels like an extravagance, a luxury that I can ill afford amidst the constant demands of WellQuest.

With a sigh, I close the fridge door, my fingers lingering on the cool metal. The darkness of the room seems to mirror the uncertainty that clouds my thoughts.

Leaving the business card on the table, I let out a soft exhale as I glance around the living room. The faint light casts a gentle glow, illuminating the everyday artifacts of our life, the

scattered toys, and the cozy blanket draped over the couch. My gaze lingers on the card, a tangible reminder of a possibility I'm not quite ready to embrace.

As I tread quietly toward the bedroom, a sense of bittersweetness washes over me. The door creaks open, revealing the scene within. Emmy's tiny form rests in the crib, her rhythmic breathing a lullaby of innocence. Nearby, Ethan's silhouette lies still, lost in dreams of his own. A pang of longing tugs at my heart as I take in the tranquility of their slumber, a stark contrast to the whirlwind that often defines my waking hours.

Slipping under the covers, I nestle into the bed beside Ethan, my fingers brushing against his arm. His warmth is a comfort, a silent reassurance that I'm not alone in this journey. Yet, the weight of my decisions, the weight of WellQuest, still lingers heavily.

As I close my eyes, my mind dances on the edge of sleep and wakefulness. Chloe's offer beckons, a tantalizing beacon of potential relief, and yet, a wariness holds me back. The room is hushed, the world beyond my thoughts quieted by the night. At this moment, I find solace in the familiar embrace of my family, even as I wrestle with the uncertainty that lies ahead.

...

The next morning arrives with the soft rays of dawn filtering through the curtains, casting a gentle glow over the room. I stir, the remnants of a restless night still clinging to my thoughts. I roll over and reach an arm out, expecting to feel Ethan's warmth beside me. Instead, I feel nothing but the soft fabric of the sheets.

He must have gone to the gym, I think to myself.

As I sit up, a knock at the door pulls me from my reverie, and I move to answer it.

There stands Lily, a bundle of energy and excitement, a box of donuts in her hands. Her bright red and purple hair frame the radiant smile on her face. Her large stomach seems to overpower the rest of her small frame as if to remind anyone who is curious that, yes, she is pregnant. Unmistakably.

"Hey there, supermom-to-be at your service!" Lily's greeting comes with a playful wink as she steps inside, her vibrant aura filling the space. "I come bearing gifts, the universal peace offering of donuts."

I chuckle, my lips curving into a more genuine smile in response to her buoyant spirit. "You really know the way to a sleep-deprived soul's heart."

As she sets the box on the kitchen counter, her eyes twinkle mischievously. "I've mastered the art of donut diplomacy."

Lily's eyes light up with a mischievous sparkle as she opens the box and pulls out a chocolate donut. She takes a bite and moans with pleasure. "Oh, Christine, you wouldn't believe the cravings I've been having lately," she raves. "It's like my taste buds have declared their independence and are staging a rebellion against my usual preferences!"

She punctuates her words with animated gestures, her hands mimicking the chaos of her cravings. "Just the other night, I found myself raiding the pantry like a stealthy snack ninja. Pickles and ice cream? Check. Peanut butter and olives? You bet. It's like my pregnancy hormones are running a gourmet rollercoaster through my kitchen."

Her laughter bubbles over, infectious and genuine. But then my gaze drifts toward my office door. It's as though my work is beckoning me to begin. I do my best to be present for my friend anyway. "Peanut butter and olives?" I say. "Seriously?"

Lily shrugs, a mischievous grin playing on her lips. "Desperate times call for daring culinary experiments, my friend. You'd be surprised how strangely satisfying it can be."

We share a laugh, and I can't help but admire her radiant glow. Her pregnancy is a badge of honor she wears proudly, a reminder of the incredible journey she's embarking upon. Yet, as she starts recounting her latest escapades, the midnight cravings that have her raiding the fridge, and the hilarious mix-ups caused by pregnancy brain, my mind starts to wander. My eyes drift to the round clock that hangs in the kitchen.

It's already nine? I realize. *I should be getting started.*

I nod and offer the occasional chuckle, trying to muster the same level of engagement that Lily is offering so freely. Her stories are undoubtedly amusing, and any other day, I'd be right there with her, swapping anecdotes and laughing till our bellies hurt. But today, my thoughts are an unruly tide, tugging me away from the present moment.

Lily's voice finally breaks through my reverie, her expression shifting from animated storytelling to a concerned friend. "Hey, you okay?" she asks. "You seem a million miles away."

I blink, my gaze refocusing on her, and guilt creeps in at having let my distraction show. "Sorry, Lily. I'm just... you know, a bit scattered today."

Her brow furrows, a mixture of empathy and curiosity dancing in her eyes. "Christine, you can always talk to me. That's what friends are for."

I sigh, appreciating her genuine concern. "I know, Lily. It's just... WellQuest stuff, you know? It's been a whirlwind lately."

Lily looks at me for a moment and then gestures to the box of donuts. "Have a donut," she says. She plops down on the barstool and leans on the counter. "Relax with me for a minute," she adds.

I shake my head. "You know I don't eat that stuff," I tell her. I jab a thumb at my office door, "*Wellness coach*, remember?"

But Lily's insistence is unwavering, her eyes twinkling with a mixture of playfulness and determination. "Come on, Christine, you've got to indulge a little. It's the unofficial rule of pregnancy, cravings are the boss, and friends need to support!"

She places a colorful donut in front of me, its sugary glaze catching the light like a sweet temptation. I hesitate, my mind warring between my ingrained preference for healthy choices and the allure of breaking free, if only for a moment. Part of me resists, clinging to the familiar routine that's been my anchor for so long.

Lily's laughter rings out, a knowing chuckle that echoes my internal struggle. "Trust me, one donut won't undo all your wellness wizardry. Sometimes, you've got to let go and embrace the sweetness of life."

Her words resonate, a reminder that rigidity isn't always synonymous with balance. With a reluctant smile, I pick up the donut, its soft texture yielding beneath my touch. As I take a tentative bite, the burst of sugary delight dances on my taste buds, a pleasant surprise that sparks a mixture of guilt and indulgence.

Lily watches with a satisfied grin, her victory evident in the triumph of a single bite. "See? Not so bad, right?"

I chuckle, my resistance melting away as I savor the unexpected treat. "Okay, you win," I admit.

"Right, I always do," Lily says. But then her gaze meets mine, her brow furrowing slightly. "But, now it's time to spill the beans. What's going on?"

I let out a sigh, a mixture of frustration and exhaustion escaping with it. "Oh, you know, the usual chaos. Brownsville Elementary speech, law firm presentation, doctor's office posters, gym collaboration, personalized fitness plans, it's like I'm juggling more tasks than there are hours in a day."

Lily raises an eyebrow, her expression a mix of sympathy and empathy. "That does sound like a lot. Have you considered getting some help? You don't have to do it all alone, you know."

A hint of resistance prickles within me, a stubborn belief that I should be able to handle it all on my own. "No, I can manage it on my own. Plus, I'm not sure I want to invest in hiring someone."

Lily leans forward, her eyes locking onto mine with a determined glint. "Chris, think about it. An extra pair of hands could make a world of difference. Someone who can take care of the nitty-gritty details, leaving you more time to focus on the bigger picture."

Her words linger in the air, a seed of possibility taking root in my mind.

Could I really let go of some control and bring someone else into the fold? I wonder. *Could I trust them to uphold WellQuest's vision as passionately as I do?*

The idea begins to take shape, the weight of my responsibilities seeming just a bit lighter. "You might be onto something, Lily. Maybe it's time to consider finding an assistant, someone who shares our values and can help take some of the load off my shoulders."

Lily grins, her eyes shining with encouragement. "Exactly! You're a guru, Chris, but even the best need a bit of support now and then."

A chuckle escapes me, a sense of relief mingling with a newfound sense of determination. "Alright, I'll start looking into it. Thanks, Lily. You always know how to bring clarity to the chaos."

As our conversation continues, a renewed sense of purpose takes hold. Lily's words have ignited a spark, reminding me that seeking help isn't a sign of weakness, it's a smart move toward ensuring that WellQuest can thrive and grow without sacrificing my own well-being.

After a while, Lily and I exchange a warm hug, her words of encouragement lingering in the air like a comforting melody.

"You've got this, Christine. Just remember, a little help can go a long way," she tells me.

I offer a grateful smile, feeling a renewed sense of purpose settling within me. "Thank you, Lily. I'll keep that in mind."

As Lily heads out, I turn my attention to the soft cries echoing from the other room. *Emmy's awake*, I think.

Her wails tug at my heart, and with quick strides, I reach her crib. Gently lifting her into my arms, I offer soothing words and gentle pats, but her cries persist.

"Come on, little one," I coo, but it only makes her cries grow louder.

With a heavy sigh, I carry her to the living room, the glow of the TV casting a soft light across the room.

"Quiet now, it's okay," I say in my most soothing voice, doing my best to calm her down. But, she only begins to squirm in my arms.

My gaze flickers to the television, where the vibrant colors and playful characters of *Cocomelon* are playing.

I bite my lip, not wanting to take the easy way out, but I know that I have work to do. I place Emmy down on the floor among a pile of pillows, blankets, and toys. She continues to wail until her eyes find the colorful screen. A sense of relief washes over me as her cries gradually subside, replaced by an intrigued calmness.

I watch Emmy, her tiny fingers reaching out as if trying to touch the characters on the screen. The soft melodies of the show fill the room, creating a cocoon of tranquility around my daughter.

A twinge of guilt tugs at my heart as I watch Emmy's eyes remain fixated on the screen, the colorful characters dancing across it. It's a familiar internal struggle, the push and pull between the demands of my business and the responsibilities of motherhood. A sigh escapes me, a mixture of conflicting emotions swirling within.

I know I should be engaging with Emmy, playing and interacting with her, but the weight of the tasks ahead feels almost insurmountable.

I grab my laptop from my office and bring it into the living room. I settle onto the couch, sitting cross-legged, and place the laptop before me. With one eye on Emmy, I open the device with a determined focus.

The glow of the screen bathes my face as I begin my search for the perfect employee, someone who can share my vision for WellQuest, someone who can help shoulder the burden that threatens to overwhelm me.

The day stretches on, the soft glow of the laptop casting a solitary aura in the dimly lit room. I comb through profiles, resumes, and cover letters, each candidate a potential piece in the puzzle that is my growing business. It's a meticulous process, a careful balance of skills and values, each decision carrying the weight of WellQuest's future.

As the hours tick by, my eyes grow heavy with fatigue, and my search becomes both a mission and a haze. The world outside seems to fade as I delve deeper into the digital realm, my determination driving me forward even as exhaustion nips at my edges.

Finally, I find her.

The perfect candidate.

I send her an email with a hopeful smile. As I do, Emmy's soft coos remind me why I am doing this. With an employee, I can hopefully focus more on my family life. *Right?* This search is a step toward building a better future, not just for WellQuest, but for Emmy too.

Reflections

How do the elements of this chapter relate to your business?

Actions to Take

1 _____

2 _____

3 _____

CHAPTER 4

FABULOUS BUT FORGETFUL

A week later, I stand by the window. Anticipation thrums through me, setting my heart aflutter. The morning sun bathes the world outside in a soft, golden glow, casting a warm embrace over the scene. My gaze is fixed on the driveway, my eyes tracing the path that will lead my chosen candidate to our doorstep. Today marks a new chapter, a step closer to reshaping my reality.

My mind races with a mixture of excitement and nerves. I wonder about the person about to enter my world, the individual who will become an integral part of the WellQuest journey.

Will they bring fresh perspectives and innovative ideas? I wonder. *Can they feel the heartbeat of our mission, the essence of what we strive to achieve?*

I pivot on my heels, the soft rustling of my steps a mere echo against the backdrop of bubbling laughter. My heart skips a beat as I take in the scene in the kitchen. My mother, her hair tied back into a loose bun, feeding Emmy her breakfast with an air of effortless grace. My daughter's giggles ripple through the air like a melody, a symphony of pure joy that fills the room.

Emmy's eyes twinkle with delight, her tiny hands reaching out to grasp the spoon, her laughter a testament to the simple pleasures of this moment. As I watch them, a complex surge of emotions tugs at my heartstrings, a mixture of awe and yearning intertwining within me.

Amidst Emmy's contagious giggles, this weird feeling gnaws at me, like a sour taste in my brain. As she laughs and laughs, it strikes me that I was not the reason for her happy sounds. Guilt and resentment bubble up.

Why doesn't she ever giggle for me like that? I wonder, frowning.

Just then the doorbell jingles, and I jump a little in surprise. With an eager smile, I swing the door open. On my doorstep stands a young girl, her excitement palpable in the way her eyes light up and her smile dances across her face. Long, sun-kissed blonde hair cascades down her shoulders, framing her youthful features with a touch of carefree elegance. Behind a pair of stylish glasses, her eyes shimmer with a blend of nervous anticipation and eager curiosity.

"Hello," I say, reaching out a hand. "You must be Emily Dana. Come on in!"

She shakes my hand I gesture for her to step into my home. I point toward the kitchen, where Emmy is still giggling.

"That is my mother and my daughter, Emmy," I tell Emily.

She holds up a hand and gives my mother a nervous smile. "It's nice to meet you," Emily says.

My mother nods before looking back down to scoop another spoonful of food for Emmy. "The office is this way," I tell Emily.

She follows me into the room and I shut the door behind us to drown out the noise from the kitchen.

I sigh and sit down in my computer chair. It lets out a soft *creak* as I sit cross-legged, my yellow yoga pants stretching comfortably over my legs as I do.

Emily shuffles from foot to foot. I notice that a tailored pair of charcoal-gray slacks hugs her legs, providing a sleek foundation that allows her to move freely. The fabric's subtle stretch ensures comfort throughout the day, a nod to her active lifestyle.

Going off that, I decide to start the conversation. "So, I see on your resume that you're pretty passionate about wellness too?"

Emily chuckles, loosening up. A genuine warmth radiates from her expression. "Oh, absolutely. I'm a firm believer in the power of wellness to transform not just our bodies, but our entire lives. It's like a puzzle, you know?" She pauses to adjust her glasses. "All these different pieces, physical, mental, emotional, all coming together to create a picture of well-being."

A grin tugs at the corners of my lips, my heart warming at the resonance of their words. "I couldn't agree more. It's like you're speaking my language. Wellness isn't just a job for me, it's a mission. I've seen firsthand how it can change lives, and that's what WellQuest is all about."

Emily's eyes light up, a spark of connection igniting between us. "That's amazing. It's rare to find someone who gets it on such a deep level. I've always believed that when you're aligned with your passion, work doesn't feel like work anymore."

We share a laugh, and it's like a secret handshake of understanding. At that moment, I feel hopeful that I made the right choice to hire her.

With a friendly grin, I reach toward my desk and pick up a piece of paper that I've been scribbling on all morning. I the sheet of paper her way with a trusting smile. "So, this is what I need you to do today," I tell her.

Her gaze lands on the paper, and a hint of surprise dances across her features. "Oh, wow, this is quite a list," she remarks, a mix of curiosity and uncertainty tinging her voice.

I chuckle softly, momentarily absorbed in my own mental checklist. "Yeah, it's a bit of a juggling act, but I've got confidence in you."

Emily's shoulders give a subtle shrug, her attention captured by the array of tasks before her. "S-sure thing," she stutters. "I'll dive right in."

The list itself is a medley of responsibilities, a snapshot of the day's endeavors that span the spectrum of our wellness pursuit. At the forefront, there's the task of confirming the assembly time with the school, an essential piece of the puzzle for our upcoming engagement. Tucked alongside is the need to draft an invoice for the doctor's office, a meticulous dance of numbers and details. And not to be forgotten, the virtual realm beckons as well, with a slew of direct messages on Instagram waiting for a thoughtful reply. It's all important work, but nothing that one person couldn't handle.

I turn to my computer, eager to begin writing a script for my next wellness video to upload to the website. Out of the corner of my eye, I watch as Emily settles down at the little table that I set up for her at the opposite end of the room. She powers up my spare laptop and leans in, engrossed in the work.

Good, I think. *She seems to know what to do.*

I settle into work, my mind feeling free of worries, knowing that I have someone to help me with the small tasks to do.

After a while, I glance up from my computer screen to see Emily walking toward me with the laptop in her arms.

"Okay, uhm, so Christine, I've got the invoice for the doctor's office ready for you to review," she says, her voice a mix of eagerness and a hint of uncertainty.

My curiosity piqued, and I motion for her to continue. Emily shows me a document, her eyes watching intently for my reaction. As I skim through the lines, my brow furrows in frustration. "Emily, this isn't right. Not at all," I say, frustration leaking through my voice. "It needs to be more streamlined, with specific sections for different charges. This is… garbage."

Her shoulders slump slightly, a hint of disappointment shadowing her expression. "Oh, I'm sorry, I thought I had it right."

Anger bubbles in my mind, but I take a deep breath. *Practice what you teach*, I remind myself. Surely, Emily didn't know how I like things done. *How could she have read my mind?* I remind myself.

A sigh escapes my lips, her mistake still gnawing at my patience, but my mind slowly composing itself. "No worries, but we need to make sure it's done correctly. It's a vital piece of our professionalism," I tell Emily, a lingering and an unintended edge still in my voice.

Emily's gaze drops, and I sense her deflation. "I'll fix it right away," she mumbles, her voice tinged with disappointment.

I take another calming breath, realizing I need to address the situation more constructively. "Emily, let's work on this together, okay? I'll show you the preferred format, and we'll make sure it's all good to go."

Her eyes meet mine, a mix of gratitude and relief in her gaze. "Thank you, Christine. I appreciate your guidance."

I manage a reassuring smile, and tell her, "Of course, Emily. We're a team, and we'll get this sorted out together."

With a renewed sense of purpose, we huddle around the desk, side by side, the glow of the computer screen illuminating our joint effort. As I guide Emily through the proper formatting steps, I can almost feel the tension lifting from the room.

I watch closely as Emily leans in, her eyes fixed on the computer screen as I guide her through the steps of formatting the invoice. "Alright, so you see how we divide the charges into categories?'" I explain, my voice patient and encouraging.

Emily nods her expression a mix of concentration and determination. "Yes, I've got it now. It looks much clearer this way."

A small smile tugs at the corners of my lips. "Exactly. It's all about making it easy to read and understand."

With newfound confidence, Emily takes the reins, her fingers dancing across the keyboard as she follows the steps. "There, I think it's coming together."

I lean back in my chair, genuinely impressed. "You're a quick learner, Emily. Great job."

Her face lights up, a mixture of pride and relief washing over her. "Thank you, Christine. I appreciate your help"

As we wrap up the invoice, Emily's enthusiasm is palpable. "You know, Christine, I was thinking... What if we did a video for your website? Something like healthy recipe ideas to promote wellness. It could be really engaging and valuable for your audience."

I pause, struck by the idea. "You know what, Emily? That's a fantastic idea. Let's do it."

Maybe having an employee isn't so bad after all, I think. *I mean, she's already coming up with good ideas.*

With a shared sense of excitement, we set up the camera, props, and ingredients. I stand in front of the lens, feeling a mix of nerves and anticipation. "Alright, here we go," I say, giving Emily a thumbs-up.

She operates the camera with ease, capturing every step as I talk through the recipe. Surprisingly, the words flow effortlessly, and the process feels natural. As I finish, I glance over at Emily, who's nodding with an encouraging smile.

"Cut! That was fantastic, Christine," she exclaims, her enthusiasm infectious.

We review the footage together, and to my surprise, it's smooth and engaging. "Wow, Emily, you've got a knack for this. Thank you for the idea."

She blushes modestly and adjusts her glasses. "I'm glad you liked it," she says quietly.

I glance at the clock. "Wow," I say with surprise, "Time is really ticking by today." I turn to Emily again and ask, "Hey, did you get a chance to call the school and confirm the assembly time?"

Emily hesitates, her gaze briefly dropping. "Oh, I'm sorry, Christine. I got caught up with the video, and I completely forgot."

What? I think, a brick dropping into my gut. *She didn't confirm the time?*

"That was on your to-do list!" I say, my voice louder than expected. "Emily, *come on!* That was a crucial task. We needed that confirmation!"

Her expression reflects genuine remorse, and I can see the weight of her mistake settling in. "I know, I messed up. I'm really sorry."

My voice tinges with exasperation, the mounting pressures of the day converging at this moment. "We can't afford oversights like this, Emily."

I quickly dial the school's number, my heart racing as I wait for Principal Andrews to pick up. The sound of the ringing seems to stretch on, each second ticking by like an eternity. Finally, a voice comes through the line.

"Hello, this is Principal Andrews."

"Hi, Principal Andrews, it's Christine from WellQuest," I say, my voice a mixture of urgency and relief.

"Hello, Christine. We're all looking forward to your presentation," Principal Andrews responds, his tone attentive.

I gather my thoughts, the urgency of the situation propelling my words. "I just wanted to confirm the time for the assembly."

There's a brief pause on the other end, and I hold my breath, hoping for a quick confirmation. "Of course, Christine. The assembly starts in half an hour, so please ensure you're here on time."

My heart skips a beat as I process the information. *Only a half hour?* I start to panic. "Got it, Principal Andrews," I say in a falsely calm voice. "I will be there in time to set up."

"Excellent. Looking forward to your presentation," he replies, his voice warm and encouraging.

I hang up the phone with a sense of urgency, realizing that time is of the essence.

"Half an hour," I mutter to myself, a mix of determination and a hint of nerves coursing through my veins.

Fury courses through my veins, a surge of adrenaline propelling me into action. I can't afford to waste a moment.

"I'll be back," I snap at Emily, my words terse and charged.

Without waiting for a response, I grab my coat and rush towards the door. The urgency of the situation fuels my steps as I practically bolt out of the house. Time is slipping away, and I refuse to let this misstep derail our efforts.

The world outside blurs as I navigate the streets with single-minded determination. My mind is a whirlwind of thoughts, a relentless mantra of 'I have to make it on time' repeating in my head. Every passing second feels like a countdown, a ticking clock that threatens to sabotage the presentation we've worked so hard for.

...

The familiar sound of my front door closing behind me seems to echo through the quiet house, signaling my return. The exhaustion that has settled into my bones is almost tangible, a heavy weight that tugs at every step I take.

What a day, I think as I walk through the dimly lit hallway. As I move forward, the events of the day play like a movie reel in my mind.

Even though I was almost late, I ended up arriving at Brownsville Elementary on time. The presentation went well, a successful culmination of days of hard work, perfecting the speech. The sense of accomplishment should have been invigorating, but the reality of my responsibilities tugged me back into the fray.

As I walk into the dark kitchen, my thoughts turn to the unexpected twist that awaited me after the presentation. A last-minute consultation with a client at the gym had demanded my attention, forcing me to drive across town just as my day was winding down. The clock had ticked away mercilessly, the consultation stretching into the late hours of the night.

The memory of that prolonged meeting lingers, a reminder of the sacrifices I make in pursuit of the goals I've set for myself and WellQuest. The late-night drive back home had been a solitary journey, the small town lights blurring into a stream of colors as weariness settled over me like a shroud.

I lean against the wall, my eyes flickering as I struggle to keep them open. Emily hadn't been a help, after all. She messed up the invoice, she forgot to call the school. *She made things worse, not better,* I realize. The work isn't that hard, why couldn't she just get it done?

Suddenly the piercing cries of Emmy cut through the hushed stillness of the night, jolting me alert. With a weary sigh, I push myself toward the bedroom, the fatigue of the day still clinging to my limbs.

I navigate the darkened corridor, my steps guided by a mix of familiarity and parental instinct. The soft glow of the moon filters through the windows, casting gentle shadows along the path. As I enter the cozy warmth of the bedroom Emmy's cries intensify, a heartrending chorus that echoes my own weariness.

Gently cradling her in my arms, I offer a soft, soothing murmur, my voice a calming presence amid the storm of her distress. I move out of the bedroom, hoping to allow Ethan's sleeping form in the bed a few more moments of sleep before he hears her.

I go back into the kitchen. My fingers deftly warm a bottle of milk, the gentle clinks of glass against glass punctuating the quiet. Emmy's cries gradually wane, her tiny form nestling against me as I settle into a chair. The rhythmic creak of the chair seems to mirror the rhythm of my own exhaustion.

My weary gaze sweeps across the cluttered kitchen counter, a landscape of scattered dishes and half-finished tasks. My gaze freezes on something unexpected, a small rectangle of paper.

Chloe's business card, I realize.

The exhaustion that clings to my bones seems to amplify the bold letters printed on the card, each word a reminder of the potential for change.

With Emmy nestled against me, her tiny form a bundle of warmth and innocence, I reach for the card, my fingers tracing its edges almost reverently. The weight of my responsibilities presses heavily on my shoulders, an unrelenting reminder of the demands that stretch me thin.

A sigh escapes my lips, a mixture of weariness and determination. With Chloe's offer of assistance echoing in my mind, a flicker of hope dances in my fatigued heart. As Emmy continues to feed, her rhythmic suckling a soothing backdrop to my thoughts, I decide that it's time to take a step towards relieving this burden.

Not only do I want to find a way to ease the responsibilities of my business, but I also want to be able to spend more time with my daughter. I've missed a few milestones in her life already and I don't want to miss any more.

The soft glow of my phone screen illuminates my face as I type out a message to Chloe, requesting a meeting. The simple act of reaching out feels like a lifeline, a lifeline that promises the possibility of easing the weight that threatens to overwhelm me.

Emmy's contented sighs mingle with the soft sound of the message being sent, a symphony of gentle moments that punctuate this quiet revelation. With the message delivered, a sense of anticipation settles over me, mingling with fatigue and hope.

As I cradle Emmy in my arms, a sense of purpose blossoms within me, a recognition that seeking help is not a sign of weakness, but rather a testament to my commitment to both my family and my dreams. With Chloe's guidance on the horizon, the path ahead seems a little less daunting, and for the first time in a while, I allow myself to entertain the notion that there might be a way to balance it all.

Reflections

How do the elements of this chapter relate to your business?

Actions to Take

1 _____

2 _____

3 _____

CHAPTER 5

CHARTING THE COURSE

Finally, I think to myself as I stretch out on the mat on the floor of my office, *a moment to do yoga.*

Each movement is a deliberate exhale, a release of tension and stress that has been accumulating within me. The muted morning light filters through the windows, casting a gentle glow that seems to echo the serenity I'm striving to cultivate.

With each controlled breath, I feel the tightness in my muscles yield, replaced by a soothing sense of flexibility. The rhythmic flow of my practice serves as a soothing balm for my weary body and mind. As I settle into the final pose, a sense of calm washes over me, a fleeting respite from the demands that constantly tug at my attention.

A gentle chime from my watch nudges me back to reality, a reminder that time is ticking steadily forward. With a final stretch and a deep breath, I conclude my yoga session, a renewed clarity infusing my thoughts. I rise from the mat, the cool floor underfoot a grounding sensation that tethers me to the present moment.

My gaze drifts to the clock on the wall, its steady hands pointing to the impending hour. A surge of gratitude courses through me as I realize that I managed to carve out this time, a few precious hours set aside amidst the clamor of responsibilities. Chloe's impending arrival looms on the horizon, a beacon of possibility and change.

Ring!

The sound of the doorbell reverberates through the house, a sound that instantly perks up my senses. Anticipation bubbles within me as I envision Chloe's arrival, ready to dive into the discussions that could potentially reshape my business and my life. With a quick glance at the clock, I acknowledge that our meeting is right on schedule.

I move towards the door, my steps tinged with excitement and swing it open with an expectant smile. However, instead of Chloe, I'm met with the warm smile of my mother, standing there with a plush elephant held in her arms.

"Oh, hi, Mom," I say. "Thank you for coming, I have an important meeting starting soon."

"Of course," she responds as she steps inside. "I'll take any time I get to spend more time with my granddaughter." My mother's eyes twinkle with affection as she holds up the stuffed toy. "I got her a little something."

Suddenly the distant sound of Emmy's cries drifts from the bedroom. My mother's gaze flickers towards the source of the sound, and we share a knowing look. We follow the sound of the cries.

Picking up my daughter from her crib, I hold her close, murmuring soothing words and gently swaying in a rhythmic attempt to comfort her. But despite my efforts, her cries persist, a reminder of the challenges that come with parenthood.

A mix of frustration and helplessness washes over me, the weight of my own exhaustion mingling with the ache of not being able to immediately console her.

"Come on now," I coo, "that's enough tears."

In the midst of my efforts, my mother steps forward. "Let me try," she says.

With a knowing smile, she takes Emmy into her arms, offering her the plush elephant toy that she brought. As the soft fabric touches Emmy's tiny fingers, a shift in her cries becomes palpable. The wails gradually give way to soft whimpers, and then, miraculously, silence.

My gaze remains fixed on the scene before me, Emmy nestled contentedly in my mother's arms, her once-distressed cries now replaced by a sense of calm. It's a bittersweet sight, one that elicits a mixture of emotions within me. There's relief that Emmy has found comfort, but also a pang of sadness that I couldn't provide it myself.

Why can't I calm my daughter like that? I wonder. *Why does she stop crying for her?*

As my mother gently cradles Emmy, I can't help but marvel at the seamless way she steps into the role of comforter. I shake my head as I leave the bedroom, a feeling of bitterness radiating through my body.

That's what Chloe is coming here for, I remind myself as I step into the kitchen. *To make it easier for me to spend time with my family.*

Speaking of having more time, my mind suddenly shifts to my new employee. I glance at the clock and realize that Emily was meant to arrive ten minutes ago.

Where is she? I think.

Ring!

The doorbell chimes again. I go to answer it, unsure of whether to expect my employee or Chloe.

It's Chloe.

She stands at my doorstep, her sleek, white hair perfectly framing her gentle face. She has one hand on her hip, seemingly to showcase her perfectly tailored suit. Her other hand clutches a large briefcase, showing that she came well-prepared. A warm smile lights up her features as she steps inside, and I feel a glimmer of reassurance wash over me.

"Hi, Christine! It's great to see you," Chloe greets me, her words infused with genuine warmth. "Your home is lovely."

"Thank you, Chloe," I reply, my own smile mirroring her friendliness. "Please, come in. Let's head to my home office."

As we make our way through the familiar hallways, I lead Chloe into my workspace. My cheeks redden as I watch Christine take in the messy surroundings and post–it–covered walls.

We settle into the chairs, the atmosphere a blend of purpose and curiosity. My gaze meets Chloe's as I take a deep breath, ready to dive into the heart of our conversation.

"So, Chloe, I've been thinking a lot about your offer to help redefine WellQuest," I begin my voice a mixture of eagerness and vulnerability. "The truth is, I'm feeling overwhelmed, and I know I need to make changes. But I'm not quite sure where to begin."

Chloe leans forward slightly, her eyes attentive and empathetic. "I understand, Christine. It's completely natural to feel that way, especially when you're juggling so much. The first step is identifying the pain points and areas that need improvement. We'll work together to pinpoint those and create a plan that aligns with your vision for WellQuest."

She rests her briefcase on a spare corner of my desk and opens it up. She pulls out a large sketchpad and props it up against my computer monitor.

"The first thing I do with a new client is to create a flowchart to identify your business' structure," she says, holding up an array of colorful Sharpie markers. "Putting everything into a visual will help us identify areas that require playbooks, step-by-step instructions, and checklists."

I nod. "I see," I say. "I guess this will help me get a better look at what tasks need to be done?"

Chloe nods. "Precisely. By mapping everything out, you are more likely to become organized."

She opens the cap of a blue Sharpie, the pungent scent filling the room. The marker makes a satisfying *squeak* as she draws a line on the sketchpad.

"Alright, Christine," Chloe begins with a determined smile. "Let's start with Social Media Content. This seems to be a significant part of your business. We'll break it down into two components: Content Planning and Content Creation."

As Chloe's words fill the air, I feel a sense of clarity beginning to emerge. This simple act of breaking down a seemingly overwhelming task into distinct segments feels like a lifeline, a way to regain control amidst the chaos.

"Content Planning," Chloe continues, her marker gliding across the paper, "involves outlining your content strategy, deciding on themes, and planning out your posts in advance. This will give you a clear roadmap and save time in the long run."

I nod in agreement, absorbing Chloe's insights. With each stroke of the marker, the pieces of the puzzle start to come together. But it's the next part, "Content Creation," that truly captures my attention.

"We want to ensure that creating content doesn't become a constant, overwhelming effort," Chloe explains. "Instead, we'll create content in batches that can be repurposed across

multiple platforms. This way, you can schedule posts in advance, leaving you with more time for other tasks."

I let out a deep breath. The prospect of not being shackled by a never-ending stream of content creation feels like a breath of fresh air. Chloe's approach aligns perfectly with my vision of finding sustainable solutions that allow my business to thrive without consuming every waking moment.

As Chloe sketches out the process on the sketchpad, I can almost visualize the newfound efficiency taking shape. The notion of reclaiming time, of untangling myself from the clutches of day-to-day content management, is liberating.

"Christine, our goal is to transform your business structure to work for you," Chloe states firmly, her marker coming to a rest. "With this flowchart, we're establishing a foundation for streamlined processes, leaving more room for creativity and growth."

I take a moment to absorb the words and the structure before me. The flowchart represents more than just a diagram; it's a symbol of change, a tangible manifestation of the transformation I'm seeking.

As Chloe and I work together, our collaboration becomes a dance of ideas and markers, each stroke on the sketchpad bringing more clarity to the complex tapestry of WellQuest's operations.

"Let's tackle Social Media Effectiveness next," Chloe suggests, pulling out a purple Sharpie. "This involves analyzing how your social media content is performing and how it's contributing to generating new clients."

I watch as she effortlessly adds another branch to the growing web of responsibilities. "This will provide valuable insights into what's working and what needs adjustment," she explains. "It's all about data-driven decision-making."

As Chloe's marker glides, my mind races with the possibilities that data analysis can bring. It's as if we're not just organizing tasks, but orchestrating a symphony of efficiency that will resonate throughout the business.

"Another important factor is WellQuest Wellness Hub upkeep," Chloe continues, creating another branch with a green Sharpie. "This is about consistently creating new content to engage and retain your subscribers. We'll establish a content calendar to keep things organized."

I find myself nodding enthusiastically, appreciating how Chloe's methods align with my desire for a structure without sacrificing creativity.

We move through the flowchart, adding each element with precision and purpose. Time seems to pass by in a whirlwind as Chloe picks out new colors of Sharpie to add new branches to the paper.

"Client Intake Process: The step-by-step process for onboarding new clients," Chloe articulates, capturing the essence of each stage with her markers.

"Scheduling and Appointment Management," I chime in, joining her in mapping out the intricacies of managing appointments and ensuring a seamless client experience.

"Client Follow-up and Support: How WellQuest maintains ongoing communication with clients," Chloe adds, emphasizing the importance of maintaining relationships beyond the initial engagement.

"Quality Control and Feedback Loop," I continue. I take the initiative by picking up an orange Sharpie to trace the loop that ensures our services are not only meeting but exceeding expectations.

"Financial Management," Chloe concludes, drawing connections that showcase the financial flow of the business.

With each addition, the flowchart evolves into a comprehensive map of WellQuest's operations.

"Okay," Chloe finally says, putting down her last Sharpie. I can practically see the steam being released from its tip as if it had been running on fumes.

As we step back to admire our work, I'm struck by the realization that we've created more than just a visual aid. We've crafted a road map to transform my business into a well-oiled machine, finely tuned for growth and sustainability.

"Our goal," Chloe says with a satisfied smile, "is to give you a clear overview of how everything fits together and where there's room for optimization."

I can't help but echo her smile. This flowchart represents a new era for WellQuest, one where order and strategy replace chaos and overwhelm. And as we continue to refine and innovate, I'm excited for the future that's unfolding before my eyes.

I turn to Chloe, who is patting down her white hair with a satisfied smile.

"Hey," I say, "why don't I whip us up some healthy smoothies to celebrate our progress?" She grins. "That sounds like a wonderful idea."

Reflections

How do the elements of this chapter relate to your business?

Actions to Take

1 _____

2 _____

3 _____

CHAPTER 6

FOLLOWING THE PATH

I navigate my way to the kitchen, reaching for an array of colorful fruits and nutritious ingredients. The sound of the blender echoes through the space, a symphony of anticipation for the treat to come.

With the flowchart completed, a tangible sense of accomplishment fills the air. It's as if the lines and shapes on the sketchpad have taken on a life of their own, embodying the structured path forward for WellQuest.

Mango, spinach, and banana, a vibrant palette of flavors that promises not only a delicious taste but also a boost of energy. With practiced ease, I measure out the ingredients, blending them into a harmonious concoction. The aroma of fresh fruits fills the air, a fragrant reminder of nature's bounty.

Chloe joins me in the kitchen as I pour the smoothies into tall glasses. It's almost as if the vibrant green hue of the mixture reflects the vitality that this partnership has infused into my business.

"Here's to progress and collaboration," I say, raising my glass to Chloe.

She smiles warmly, clinking her glass against mine. "To turning chaos into clarity."

With that, we take the first sips of our smoothies, the cool and invigorating flavors dancing across our taste buds. As we savor the moment, I can't help but feel grateful for the journey that has led us here. The completion of the map is not just a milestone; it's a testament to the power of teamwork and strategic planning.

Suddenly, my phone's ringtone slices through the air.

Glancing at the caller ID, I see Emily's name, and my irritation swells as I recall her tardiness.

Where has this girl been? I wonder.

With a quick swipe, I answer the call, my voice tight with the stress that has been building up.

"Emily, where are you? You were supposed to be here by now," I snap, my frustration bubbling over.

There's a hint of panic in Emily's voice as she responds, "Christine, I'm so sorry. I had a flat tire on the way and I'm stuck on the side of the road."

My irritation only deepens at her explanation. "A flat tire? Seriously? You should have checked your car before leaving."

Emily's voice wavers as she tries to explain, "I know, I know, it's just... it happened so suddenly."

Exasperation and stress meld into anger as I retort, "Look, Emily, I don't have time for this right now. I need you to get here as soon as possible. I can't do everything myself."

There's a heavy silence on the other end, and for a moment, I almost regret the sharpness of my words. But then, Emily replies with a quiet, "Okay, I'll do my best to get there."

The call ends with an abrupt click, the weight of my frustration settling heavily in the silence that follows. Just as I lower my phone, I sense Chloe's gaze on me, her expression a mixture of concern and disapproval. The scrutiny feels uncomfortable like a spotlight highlighting my own shortcomings.

Chloe's voice is gentle, yet laced with curiosity, as she asks, "Is everything alright, Christine? You seem a bit... tense."

I offer a strained smile, my embarrassment making it difficult to meet her eyes. "Yeah, it's just a minor hiccup with my employee."

Chloe's eyebrow arches slightly, and I can practically feel her questioning my response. She takes a slow sip of her smoothie and then leans against the kitchen counter.

"Would you mind sharing what happened? Maybe I can offer some perspective," She probes further, her tone careful.

Reluctantly, I spill the details of the call, my words tinged with lingering frustration. As I recount the situation, I become acutely aware of how trivial my reaction sounds when verbalized. The enormity of my irritation, contrasted against the simple explanation Emily provided, is hard to ignore.

Chloe's expression doesn't waver, her demeanor maintaining a calm and steady presence. When I finish speaking, she responds in measured tones, "It sounds like a tough situation, but remember, we all have our moments. What matters is how we handle them."

Her words resonate, a reminder that my actions have consequences, not just for me, but for those around me. The shame I feel deepens, a humbling acknowledgment of my own imperfections. I appreciate Chloe's nonjudgmental stance, and her willingness to offer guidance.

Taking a steadying breath, I meet Chloe's gaze directly. "You're right, Chloe. I shouldn't have reacted that way. It was unprofessional."

Chloe's response is a reassuring nod. "We all make mistakes, Christine. What's important is that you're recognizing it and that you can take steps to address it. That's the mark of growth."

I nod and take a sip of my smoothie as I ponder Chloe's words. Her inquisitive gaze rests on me, her eyes probing gently.

"Tell me more about Emily," she prompts after a while, curiosity evident in her tone.

I take a moment to gather my thoughts, contemplating how to summarize my new employee's presence amidst the whirlwind of my responsibilities. "Well, she's just started here," I begin, "but I'm not entirely sure how to utilize her skills effectively."

"Come with me," Chloe says, walking back in the direction of my home office. Curiously, I follow behind her. She stops in front of the sketchpad, which is now covered with multicolored lines and circles of writing. She gestures to the map and her lips curve into a knowing smile.

"It sounds like Emily might benefit from a more defined role within the company," she says.

I lean forward, intrigued by Chloe's suggestion. I squint over all of the different topics listed on the paper and say, "That makes sense, but I'm not sure where to start."

Chloe's demeanor is reassuring. "Let's take a closer look at the responsibilities we've identified. We can assign specific areas to Emily based on her strengths and interests."

As we revisit the list, Chloe and I deliberate on the various tasks, aligning them with Emily's skills. Chloe's insights prove invaluable as she helps me see beyond the surface and identify what Emily excels at. It becomes clear that Emily's passion for wellness could be a driving force for her role.

Chloe's voice brims with encouragement as she suggests, "How about we have Emily focus on Social Media Content? Planning videos and reels, responding to direct messages, that's a great way to leverage her skills while promoting WellQuest."

I nod in agreement, impressed by Chloe's strategic approach. "That's a fantastic idea. And given her keenness, she could also tackle Social Media Effectiveness, analyzing the impact of our content."

Chloe's enthusiasm is contagious as she continues, "Exactly. And let's not forget WellQuest Wellness Hub upkeep. Creating fresh content for subscribers will engage our audience and showcase Emily's talents."

As we discuss the possibilities, I find myself inspired by Chloe's guidance. The pieces start falling into place as we allocate tasks that align with Emily's strengths. Chloe's insights have a transformative effect on my perspective, and I feel a renewed sense of purpose.

"That's not all," Chloe says, her voice resonating with conviction. "I think Emily could excel in Client Follow-up and Support. Her dedication can ensure our clients feel connected and valued."

The gears in my mind turn, absorbing Chloe's wisdom. "And let's round it off with Quality Control and Feedback Loop," Chloe suggests. "Emily's attention to detail could contribute to maintaining our service standards."

A smile tugs at my lips as I see the potential unfolding. Chloe's ability to tap into Emily's strengths has opened up a path that benefits both Emily and WellQuest.

Ring!

The doorbell's chime echoes through the house, and I instinctively rise from my seat. As I reach the front door, a quick breath escapes me, and I twist the doorknob. There stands Emily,

her long blonde hair is disheveled and her glasses are slightly crooked. Her expression mirrors the frenzy of her arrival.

"Hey," she says with a sheepish smile, her voice carrying a hint of frazzled energy. "I'm so sorry I'm late. I had a bit of a morning…"

I hold up a hand, a reassuring smile forming on my lips. "No worries at all. Life happens, right?" I chuckle, attempting to ease any tension. "I'm sorry for snapping at you before. You didn't deserve that."

Emily nods gratefully, her shoulders relaxing slightly. "Really?" she says. "Thank you for understanding."

I lean against the door frame, meeting her gaze with a friendly look. "Don't sweat it. We've all been there. Come on in."

Emily steps inside, a blend of gratitude and relief in her demeanor. I lead her to the home office, where we find Chloe sitting at my desk, writing down notes in a Moleskine notebook.

"Emily, this is Chloe. Chloe, meet Emily," I say.

Chloe smiles up at Emily and says, "Hi, Emily."

"Hi, Chloe," Emily responds her tone a mix of excitement and a touch of nervousness. She extends a hand toward Chloe, who rises from her seat to shake it.

"It's really nice to meet you," Chloe adds, her handshake firm and reassuring.

I notice Emily's eyes widen slightly, a reaction I can empathize with, meeting someone new can be a blend of exhilarating and daunting, especially when that someone is a seasoned consultant like Chloe.

"Emily, Chloe has been an incredible asset to WellQuest," I explain, my voice conveying a genuine appreciation. "She's been helping me redefine and refine our processes, so things can run more smoothly and efficiently."

Chloe gives a modest nod, and her humility is evident. "It's a team effort, for sure. Christine is learning a lot already."

I sit down and gesture for Emily to follow suit. Chloe holds up her notebook and tells Emily, "We worked together to outline what your tasks will be here at WellQuest. We redefined them to make it easier for you to follow and give you clearer instructions."

I observe from my seat as Chloe takes the lead, explaining the new roles and responsibilities she has crafted for Emily. Emily's posture, once tense and uncertain, seems to relax with every word Chloe speaks. Her eyes, which held a hint of apprehension earlier, now carry a glimmer of relief and understanding.

Chloe's skillful communication style is evident. She breaks down the tasks and expectations into manageable pieces, delivering the information with clarity and empathy. I can almost see the weight lifting off Emily's shoulders as Chloe outlines her new path within WellQuest.

As Chloe speaks, Emily nods occasionally, her expression transforming from uncertainty to genuine interest. It's as if Chloe is unveiling a map, guiding Emily through a terrain that was previously uncharted. I can sense that Emily is beginning to see the potential and the opportunities that these roles hold for her growth and contribution.

As Chloe concludes her explanation, Emily looks up at her with a mixture of gratitude and newfound confidence. "Thank you, Chloe. This sounds... well, it sounds like something I'm genuinely excited about."

Chloe's smile is infectious, radiating encouragement. "I'm glad to hear that, Emily. We're all here to support each other, and I'm confident that your strengths and passion for wellness will shine in these roles."

After another hour of preparation, Chloe takes her leave. I wave her goodbye and a renewed sense of purpose lingers in the air. The aura of collaboration and positive change she has brought into my home office has set the stage for a more streamlined and focused day ahead.

Turning my attention to Emily, I offer a warm smile. "So, Emily, how are you feeling about your new roles?"

Emily's eyes light up, her response immediate and genuine. "Honestly, Christine, I'm excited. It feels like a weight has been lifted off me. Chloe really helped me see how these tasks align with my strengths and interests."

"That's wonderful to hear," I reply, relieved that Emily is embracing the new responsibilities with enthusiasm. "Remember, if you have any questions or need any support, I'm here for you."

Emily nods, her determination evident. "I appreciate that, Christine."

With a renewed sense of purpose, we delve into the day's tasks. Emily tackles social media content planning with a fresh perspective, her creativity evident in the ideas she's putting forth. As she responds to direct messages on Instagram, I observe her interactions, her genuine engagement with our audience is a testament to her passion for wellness.

The flow of the day is remarkably different. Without the weight of overwhelming tasks, my own focus sharpens. I find myself delving into the client intake process, mapping out the seamless journey we want our clients to experience from inquiry to engagement. The process feels purposeful and energizing, a far cry from the scattered approach I'd been grappling with before.

Emily seamlessly handles client follow-ups, her communication skills shining through. Meanwhile, the quality control and feedback loop tasks are addressed with precision, ensuring that our services are continually refined based on client input.

By the time evening arrives, a sense of accomplishment fills the room. Emily looks up from her tasks, a satisfied smile on her face. "I think we're making real progress, Christine."

I nod in agreement, feeling a newfound optimism about the road ahead. "You're absolutely right, Emily. And you played a big part in that."

As Emily packs up for the day, I feel a sense of gratitude for the positive shift that has taken place. Chloe's insights and Emily's commitment have created a new rhythm within WellQuest. It's a rhythm that feels more harmonious, more balanced, and brimming with potential.

. . .

As the evening descends, I find myself sitting outside by my garden. The setting sun is casting a warm glow through the windows of our home, and a sense of calm settles over me.

I stare at the budding vegetables in the soil and reflect on the transformative power of collaboration and the importance of embracing change. It's a lesson I won't soon forget, and I'm excited to see where this newly paved path will lead us next.

I can't believe I actually have this moment to relax, I think, letting my big toe dig into the dirt. *I actually feel in control.*

With a smile, I begin to think about how I can take advantage of this free time. The handsome face of my husband pops into my mind, and I suddenly remember how hurt he had been the other day when he confronted me about being too involved with my work.

I can make it up to him now, I realize. *I can do better.*

With my mindset, I make my way into the kitchen and gather the ingredients for Ethan's favorite chicken dish. The vibrant hues of vegetables and the earthy scent of herbs fill the air, imbuing the space with a comforting familiarity. The rhythmic chopping of vegetables against the cutting board becomes a soothing background melody as I prepare the ingredients with care.

The sizzle of olive oil in the pan awakens a sense of anticipation, and I find myself fully immersed in the artistry of cooking. Each step and each gesture is deliberate, a way of channeling my intentions into the meal. The chicken breasts meet the pan with a satisfying sizzle, and the room is soon enveloped in the mouthwatering aroma of herbs and spices melding together.

As the dish simmers and flavors meld, I can't help but recall the countless times Ethan has savored this meal, his contented smile and appreciative words serving as a testament to the love and effort that go into each preparation.

Finally, the dish is ready and plated with care. The vibrant colors and exquisite aroma are a testament to the dedication I've poured into its creation. With a sense of pride, I carry the plate to the dining table, where the soft candlelight dances in harmony with the fading daylight.

Ethan walks into the room, the aroma of the meal drawing him in with an eager curiosity. His blue eyes light up as he takes in the spread before him. "Is this...?"

I nod, my own smile mirroring his excitement. "Your favorite."

"Wow," he says, genuinely shocked. He runs a hand through his blonde hair before saying, "I'll... go get Emmy."

Moments later, he straps our daughter into her high chair. We settle in the chairs next to her and begin to eat. The simple act of sharing a meal becomes an intimate bond, a way of saying "I care" without the need for words.

Emmy babbles happily in her highchair, her infectious laughter echoing through the room like a melody of pure delight. Her innocent presence adds a touch of magic to the moment, reminding us of the joy that can be found in the simplest of pleasures.

As Ethan takes a moment to savor each bite, his eyes meet mine, filled with warmth. I can sense his appreciation not just for the delicious meal before us, but for the thought and effort that I've poured into making this moment special.

"You didn't have to do all this," he says softly, a genuine smile playing on his lips.

I return the smile, my heart swelling with a mixture of love and determination. "I wanted to. I've been so caught up in everything lately, and I realized that I need to do better. For you, for us."

Ethan reaches out and takes my hand across the table, his touch a reassuring anchor in a world that often feels like a whirlwind. "You're doing great, you know," he says, his voice a gentle reminder of his unwavering support.

We share a moment, our hands intertwined, as the world outside fades away and it's just the two of us, connected by the simple act of being together. In that moment, I'm reminded of the power of these shared experiences, and the ways in which they weave the fabric of our lives and relationships.

And as we continue to eat, with Emmy's giggles providing a cheerful soundtrack, I make a silent promise to myself, to carve out more of these moments, to find a balance between the demands of my work and the precious moments with my family. Now that I have Chloe's help, I know I can do this. The chicken dinner becomes a symbol of that promise, a reminder that amidst the chaos, it's the small gestures that create the threads of connection and love that tie us all together.

...

Later, in the stillness of the night, the soft cries of Emmy pierce through the darkness, pulling me from the edges of sleep.

Here we go again, I think.

Gently, I rise from the bed. The pale moonlight casts a gentle glow, revealing Emmy's tiny form in the crib.

As I scoop Emmy into my arms and settle into the rocking chair, her cries begin to soften, replaced by the rhythmic sounds of her feeding.

Wow, I think, *she actually stopped crying.*

The world outside feels distant, and for a moment, it's just the two of us, a mother soothing her child in the tranquil hours of the night.

But then, I hear a chime from my phone. I pick it up and frown at the waterfall of notifications popping up on my screen. Emails, direct messages, and reminders are overflowing on the lock screen.

"No," I whisper as realization dawns on me.

Even though Chloe outlined what needs to be done and Emily settled into her new role seamlessly, the list of tasks still seems to be mounting up.

Emotions well up within me, an overwhelming mix of exhaustion, frustration, and uncertainty. The tears I've been holding back spill over, mingling with the soft sounds of Emmy's feeding. In this vulnerable moment, I question whether I can truly manage it all, the responsibilities that tug at me from all directions, the delicate balance between my roles as a mother, a partner, and a businesswoman.

What if I can't do this, after all? I wonder as a tear slides down my cheek. *What if I fail?*

I let my gaze drift out the window and stare at the moon. It seems to hover above me just like the long list of tasks hovering above me.

I let out a sob, feeling crushed.

Reflections

How do the elements of this chapter relate to your business?

Actions to Take

1 _____

2 _____

3 _____

CHAPTER 7

ON THE HUNT

The first rays of dawn gently filter through the curtains, casting a warm, soft glow across the room. I shuffle into the kitchen, my steps a quiet cadence against the floor. The soft hum of the kettle fills the air as I set it on the stove, the promise of a comforting cup of tea a beacon of solace in the early hours.

As I wait for the water to boil, I glance over at the living room where Emmy is already awake, her playful babbling and the cheerful crinkle of her stuffed elephant creating a symphony of innocence. She sits contently in her playpen, the morning light dancing in her wide, curious eyes. With a weak smile, I'm reminded of the simplicity of her world, a world untouched by the pressures that weigh on me.

The aroma of the brewing tea wafts through the air, mingling with the sound of Emmy's laughter. But beneath the surface, my mind is a whirlwind of thoughts. The previous night's restless hours linger in the corners of my eyes, a reminder of the weight that accompanies the demands of my responsibilities.

As I pour the steaming water into my cup, my thoughts drift to the relentless stream of tasks that clamor for my attention. The business, the presentations, the appointments, they all dance in my mind, a relentless carousel that threatens to consume me. The delicate balance between my ambitions and the desire to be present for Emmy and Ethan feels like an intricate puzzle with no clear solution.

With the cup cradled in my hands, I move to the living room and settle into a chair. The soft, soothing warmth of the tea seeps through, a balm for both my body and my racing thoughts. I watch as Emmy explores her small world with boundless curiosity, her laughter a reminder of the joy that exists outside the confines of my to-do list.

Ring!

The familiar chime of the doorbell breaks through the stillness of the room, its notes tingling in the air. I sigh softly, my weariness etched into every line of my expression. As I make my way to the door, it swings open to reveal Chloe.

"Hey, Christine," she greets me, "Are you ready for day two?"

I nod. "Of course," I say in a weak voice. "Come on in."

Chloe raises an eyebrow at me as she crosses the threshold. I shut the door behind her and then slump back down in my chair, clutching the warm cup of tea in my hand.

Chloe pats Emmy on the head before settling into a spot on the couch. She crosses her arms and looks at me with a concerned look as I sip on my tea.

"Christine, is everything alright?" she asks with a concerned voice.

I offer a tired smile, attempting to mask the whirlwind of emotions that threatens to spill over. "Yeah, it's just been a hectic morning," I reply, my voice carrying a hint of fatigue.

"Are you sure that's all? You have deep bags under your eyes," Chloe says. I bite my tongue. "Okay," I admit. "I had trouble sleeping last night."

Chloe crosses one leg of her tailored suit over the other. "Do you want to talk about it?" she asks. Chloe's presence is reassuring, her genuine concern a balm to my frazzled nerves.

"It's just... the workload," I admit, my shoulders slumping. "The list we made, the responsibilities, the constant juggling. It feels like there's always something demanding my attention."

Chloe nods, her empathy palpable. "I can imagine how overwhelming that can be," she offers gently. "It's important to remember that you don't have to carry it all alone."

I let out a rueful chuckle, a mix of exhaustion and resignation. "Easier said than done, isn't it?"

Chloe shakes her head. "Not really, Christine," she says. "You already have Emily, and she is a wonderful asset. But, clearly, one employee isn't enough."

I sip my tea and squint my eyes in her direction.

Where is she going with this? I wonder.

"What you need is to hire more staff members," Chloe announces. "The more brains you have to put on different projects, the less work there will be left."

I shake my head. "I don't know if I can afford that," I admit.

Chloe leans forward. "You don't need a lot. I suggest just one more," she says. "One more employee will help ease the workload by a lot."

She stands up and soothes out the jacket of her suit. "Come with me, let's start hunting," she said as if the decision is hers to make.

With a sigh, I follow Chloe into my home office.

She knows best, I think.

We huddle around my laptop, the glow of the screen casting a soft light across our determined faces.

"Okay, so first, what you need to understand is that new hires are made based on tasks that need to be done," Chloe says. "What are some tasks that you are ready to shed?"

I think for a moment before saying, "Data and analytics. It would be great to have someone manage schedules, finances, that sort of thing."

Chloe puts a finger to her temple, thinking. "That sounds doable. So, we just need to find someone who has the right traits and skills for those tasks.

She turns back to the computer screen. The hum of anticipation hangs in the air as we dive into the sea of online resumes, each one a potential solution to the puzzle we're trying to solve.

"Okay, let's start with these," Chloe suggests, scrolling through a list of names and credentials. "We're looking for someone who's not only skilled but also aligned with WellQuest's values."

I nod in agreement, my eyes scanning the screen as I absorb the details. "Absolutely," I say. "It's essential that this new team member complements the existing dynamic and can step in seamlessly."

We toggle between tabs, scrutinizing qualifications, work experiences, and personal statements. As we navigate through the profiles, Chloe's expertise shines through as she points out nuances and qualities I might have overlooked.

"This one seems promising," she remarks, her finger tapping on a particular resume. " It looks like he has an unwavering eye for numbers and an innate sense of organization. We can make him a go-to person for all things data and analytics."

I lean in to examine the details, my excitement growing as I see the potential alignment. "You're right, Chloe. And their passion for wellness shines through in their cover letter."

Chloe smiles a combination of encouragement and satisfaction. "That's a good sign. Let's reach out to him."

I lean forward to type out the email. As I finish, however, the distant sound of Emmy's cries tugs me away.

"One moment," I say to Chloe, moving away from the computer. I step into the next room where her wails are more distinct, finding her tiny form nestled in her crib.

"Hey there, sweetheart," I coo gently, lifting her into my arms. "What's going on?"

As I hold her close, Emmy's cries don't lessen. Rather, she continues to wail and scream. I sway gently, my whispered assurances filling the room like a soothing lullaby. "Shh, it's okay. Mommy's here." I glance at the clock and remind myself that Ethan is at work and my mother isn't available today.

Emmy's big, curious eyes meet mine as she continues to wail. I try to explain the situation to her as if she could understand. "Daddy's working hard, and Grandma's busy today, but we'll have fun together, won't we?" I offer her a tentative smile, hoping to convey reassurance even if her baby eyes can't fully comprehend.

It doesn't work, she keeps crying. I glance back at my home office, where I know Chloe is waiting.

You can't keep her waiting forever, I tell myself. *Just do something to make Emmy stop crying.*

I lay her gently on the couch, propping her up with some cushions. I switch on the TV and turn on Cocomelon again. The cheerful children's program immediately emits colorful animations and playful melodies. I watch as Emmy's cries slowly lessen. Her attention shifts from me to the screen, her little face lighting up with wonder.

Despite the brief respite that the TV provides, a pang of guilt prickles at the edges of my consciousness.

Is it wrong to rely on this electronic distraction to pacify her? I wonder, *Shouldn't I be engaging her in more interactive, hands-on activities?*

The questions swirl, echoing the internal tug-of-war that seems to accompany every choice I make as a mother.

But at this moment, as Emmy's giggles fill the room and her eyes dance with delight, I find myself grappling with a more immediate truth: sometimes, embracing the "easy way out" is simply a matter of survival.

A surge of guilt washes over me as I return to the home office and complete the hiring process for my new employee.

Reflections

How do the elements of this chapter relate to your business?

Actions to Take

1 _____

2 _____

3 _____

CHAPTER 8

CELEBRATING PROGRESS

The next day. Emily and I are side by side, each engrossed in our respective tasks. The click of keyboards and the rustle of paper create a soothing symphony of productivity.

As I type away at my laptop, crafting emails and reviewing documents, I steal a quick glance at Emily. Her concentration is unwavering as she toggles between windows, her fingers dancing across the keyboard with practiced grace. The soft glow of the computer screen casts a warm hue on her features, emphasizing the determination etched into her expression. She idly brushes a strand of her long blonde hair behind her ear as she continues to work.

The room hums with a sense of purpose, our shared dedication to our work creating a silent camaraderie that binds us in this moment. The soft rustling of papers and the occasional sigh punctuate the quiet rhythm of our tasks. It's as if the world beyond these walls has faded away, leaving only the tangible connection of our shared purpose.

Ring!

The resonant chime of the doorbell interrupts the ambient hum of the house, drawing my attention from the work before me. With a sense of anticipation, I rise from my desk and move towards the front door.

He's here! I think, excited to meet my new employee.

As the door swings open, I'm greeted by a figure standing on the threshold, a vibrant burst of energy against the backdrop of the day.

"Jack Lipton?" I ask.

"Hi there," he offers with a warm smile, extending a hand in greeting. His cropped orange hair seems to mirror the vivacity in his gaze, and the splatter of freckles across his cheeks adds to his boyish charm. I return the smile, reciprocating the handshake with a sense of camaraderie. "You must be Christine, right?"

I nod, appreciating the friendly tone in his voice. "Yes, that's me. It's great to finally meet you, Jack."

With a welcoming gesture, I guide Jack into the house, leading him toward the home office.

"This is where the magic happens," I quip, offering a friendly smile as I motion towards the desks, the computer screens, and the scattered papers that somehow manage to stay in some semblance of order. Jack chuckles in response, his eyes bright with curiosity.

"It's a pleasure to be here," he responds, genuine interest lacing his words. "Your setup is quite impressive."

I glance over at Emily, who is engrossed in her work, diligently typing away at her computer. With a fond smile, I gesture towards her. "Jack, I'd like you to meet Emily. She's been a crucial part of our team, especially in recent times."

As he gazes at Emily, a warm smile forms on Jack's lips. "Nice to meet you, Emily," he greets her, extending a friendly hand. Emily looks up from her screen, a grin spreading across her face as she reciprocates the greeting.

"Likewise, Jack," she replies with a congenial tone. "Christine has told me great things about your expertise."

With a sense of purpose, I recall the productive session Chloe and I had just yesterday, outlining the roles that Jack would take on. As I face Jack now, I'm confident in our plan and eager to share the details with him.

"Jack," I begin, my tone clear and assured, "I want to formally welcome you to the WellQuest team."

He nods, his expression a mix of enthusiasm and attentiveness. "Thank you, Christine. I'm excited to contribute."

I continue, "My consultant, Chloe, and I have worked on defining your roles to ensure they align with your strengths and the needs of the company." Taking a moment to gather my thoughts, I elaborate, "Your primary responsibilities will include Scheduling and Appointment Management. You'll be in charge of coordinating appointments between our clients and consultants, ensuring everyone's availability is considered."

I notice a spark of interest in his eyes, and I proceed with the next assignment. "Additionally, you'll be handling Financial Management. This involves managing the flow of financial transactions, from creating invoices to tracking payments and expenses."

Jack nods thoughtfully, absorbing the information. "I'm ready to dive in and make sure things run smoothly," he affirms, a determined smile forming on his face.

With a reassuring smile of my own, I respond, "I have every confidence that you'll excel in these roles, Jack. Feel free to reach out if you have any questions or need assistance along the way."

As the weight of his new responsibilities settles in, I'm reminded once again of the collective effort it takes to keep WellQuest running smoothly. With a solid team in place, I'm optimistic about the positive changes Jack's expertise will bring to WellQuest.

The rest of the day unfolds with a newfound sense of efficiency and purpose. I find myself caught in a whirlwind of positive energy as I witness Emily and Jack seamlessly diving into their assigned roles. The tasks that once seemed like an overwhelming mountain to climb are now being conquered with diligence and enthusiasm.

Emily, sitting at her workstation with focused determination, is diligently managing the social media content. Her fingers dance across the keyboard as she drafts engaging posts, plans captivating videos, and responds to direct messages with genuine care. Each action resonates with the essence of WellQuest's mission, and it's apparent that she's embracing her role with a passion I had hoped to see.

Meanwhile, Jack is engrossed in the world of scheduling and financial management. His meticulous nature is evident as he navigates through appointments, ensuring clients and consultants' availability align seamlessly. He has already developed an organized system for managing invoices, payments, and expenses, which promises to streamline our financial operations.

As the day progresses, a sense of satisfaction washes over me. I can feel the positive impact of Emily and Jack's contributions resonating throughout the office. There's an aura of collaboration and synergy in the air, as if we're all working together to create something meaningful.

Ding!

A familiar chime breaks through the ambient hum of my work, and I glance at my phone to see a text from Lily. A smile tugs at the corners of my lips as I read her words.

Hey! I miss you! What's new? It says.

The timing is uncanny, for I'm in an unusually good mood today, fueled by the positive energy that's been radiating from the office.

Seizing the moment, I decide to act on this surge of positivity.

"Hey team," I say, catching the attention of Emily and Jack. "Today's been really great. How about a little celebration?"

Emily smiles. She leans forward and raises one eyebrow as she says, "What do you have in mind?"

A smile teases the corners of my lips. "I'm throwing a little party," I say.

With my fingers dancing across the phone screen, I draft a spontaneous message to all my friends.

Hey everyone! Impromptu gathering at my place tonight. Let's catch up and unwind. Come over whenever you can!

Hitting the send button, I can almost feel the ripple of excitement and anticipation spreading through the virtual space.

...

Later, the sun's golden fingers stretch across the expanse of the backyard. A symphony of laughter and conversation dances through the air, accompanied by the rhythmic beat of classic tunes playing softly in the background.

I've set up a table in the center of the yard, decorated with a checkered tablecloth. It's overflowing with mouthwatering, healthy treats... The grill stands to the left, sending plumes of

aromatic smoke into the air. The scent of marinated meats mingling with the earthy notes of vegetable grilling transports everyone to the heart of summer.

Ethan, wearing a grin as bright as the sunshine, expertly maneuvers the grill's tongs, flipping burgers and skewers with a seasoned touch. The flames dance in harmony with his movements, casting flickering shadows on his face that mirrors the playfulness in his eyes.

Lily's laughter bubbles like a melody as she recounts a humorous incident from her day, her animated gestures emphasizing every punchline.

"And then, can you believe it, the dog actually took off with my shoe!' She says, gesturing over her pregnant belly to a torn-up flip-flop on her foot.

Alex, her partner in mischief, chuckles heartily and playfully nudges her. "Well, he wouldn't have if you didn't insist on petting him!" he says, causing the rest of the group to laugh along.

"Thank you for inviting me," Chloe leans over and says to me as the laughter simmers down.

"Of course," I tell her. "You've done so much for me, I wouldn't even be able to *breathe* if it weren't for your advice."

Chloe smiles and gestures to Emily and Jack, who are sipping beers near my garden. "You made great picks with the two of them. I think that they will really help move WellQuest along."

As the sun dips below the horizon, casting its warm embrace upon us, the scene takes on a serene and intimate quality. The soft glow of string lights drapes the gathering like a celestial canopy, infusing the evening with a magical aura.

"Christine, I must say, this barbecue is amazing," Alex remarks between bites of a perfectly grilled skewer, his approval evident in his satisfied grin.

Ethan puts an arm over my shoulder as he takes a sip of iced tea. "Hey, let's not forget who cooked the meat!" he laughs.

He turns to me and whispers in my ear. "Hey," he says, "Alex is right. This has been a great day."

I shrug and take a bite of my salad. "The new plan that Chloe helped me come up with has worked like a charm. I feel this weight off my shoulders," I admit.

Ethan kisses my cheek. His touch sends warmth throughout my body. "I'm proud of you for making those changes," he says. Then, in a more gentle tone, adds, "It really shows me that you want to make things work. With the business and with our family."

I turn to him and press my lips to his. The familiar touch sends a surge of passion through my body. For a moment, everyone else fades away. It's only my husband and I, nothing else matters.

When he pulls away he says, "I have high hopes for WellQuest, and for you. Keep this up."

I smile and say, "I will."

Suddenly, Emmy's cries pierce the air. The sudden shift in the atmosphere ripples through the gathering like a passing cloud momentarily dimming the sun.

I instinctively rise from my seat, my heart aching in response to her distress. I hurry over to the playpen, my steps quickening as I approach. Emmy's tiny form is nestled amidst plush toys and blankets, her face flushed with the telltale signs of discomfort. Gently, I scoop her into my arms, her cries resonating against my chest.

"It's alright, sweetheart," I whisper, my voice a soft melody of reassurance. I sway gently, attempting to replicate the soothing rhythm of her cradle. My fingers brush over her soft hair, and I press a tender kiss against her forehead, hoping to offer her the comfort she seeks.

Yet, despite my efforts, Emmy's cries persist, her small body trembling in my arms. I shift from side to side, hum softly, and murmur sweet words, desperate to alleviate whatever has upset her delicate world.

I look up and notice that everyone is looking at me as I struggle to calm my daughter. Emily and Jack try to hide their stares by looking away, but Lily is more direct, raising her eyebrow questioningly.

"Here, pass her to me," a voice says from behind me. I turn to see my mother standing there, her arms outstretched.

Reluctantly, I pass Emmy to her. Once she is out of my arms, Emmy's cries immediately subside.

I watch in a mixture of awe and turmoil as Emmy's tiny fingers curl around my mother's finger, her sobs gradually softening into whimpers.

While my heart should swell with gratitude at my mother's ability to bring comfort, a pang of sadness infiltrates my emotions.

Why her? I wonder, my cheeks reddening with embarrassment.

For all my efforts, all the sleepless nights, and unrelenting determination, it's my mother who holds the key to soothing Emmy's tears.

Emmy's cries finally yield to a hushed sigh, her small form nestled against my mother's nurturing embrace. I force a smile, masking the turmoil within me.

The recent strides in redefining WellQuest have made a world of difference in my life, that much is true. The streamlined processes, the roles that are now thriving under competent hands, and the vibrant energy that pulses through the team, it all impacted my life in incredible ways so far.

Yet, even amidst this mosaic of progress, a sobering realization settles in: the journey is far from over.

With a heavy sigh, I allow my thoughts to drift. As I watch Emmy's innocent laughter ripple through the air, I'm reminded that in the midst of professional endeavors, there's a constant balancing act, a dance between the demands of the business and the yearning for a meaningful connection with those I hold dear.

This has been one step down, I think to myself, *many more to go.*

Reflections

How do the elements of this chapter relate to your business?

Actions to Take

1 _____

2 _____

3 _____

CHAPTER 9

SUNLIGHT AND SCORECARDS

The next day, under the open sky, bathed in the warmth of the sun's embrace, Chloe and I find ourselves seated in my garden. The gentle breeze plays with the tendrils of my hair as we share this tranquil moment, a lull in the symphony of life's demands.

Leaning back against the cushioned chair, I offer a grateful smile, appreciating the space she's created for reflection. The vibrant colors of blooming flowers frame our conversation, an unspoken reminder of growth and change.

Chloe's voice breaks the silence, her words gentle yet brimming with anticipation. "Christine," she begins, her gaze unwavering, "are you ready for the next step?"

A wistful smile tugs at the corners of my lips as I respond, my voice carrying a blend of reflection and aspiration. "Chloe, these past days have been a journey of transformation, of peeling back layers and embracing change. I've watched WellQuest evolve and, in turn, I've seen parts of myself adapt and grow."

The garden seems to hold its breath. Chloe's serene demeanor encourages me to continue.

With renewed determination, I turn my gaze to the horizon, the sky a canvas for dreams yet to be realized.

Thinking about my realization at the barbecue last night, I say, "Yes, Chloe," I say, a surge of resolve coursing through me. "I'm ready for the next step. What is it?"

"Scorecards," Chloe says with a smile.

She bends down to open the briefcase that rests against the legs of her chair. She opens it and pulls out her laptop, which she sets on the iron outdoor table between us.

"The first thing you need to know is about KPIs or key performance indicators," Chloe says as the laptop powers on. "This is an essential tool for measuring WellQuest's progress."

The soft rustling of leaves in the breeze seems to echo our conversation as Chloe leans in and continues, "Christine, KPIs are like a compass that helps us navigate the vast sea of data and goals. They provide us with measurable markers to track how well we're doing in various areas."

As her words weave a web of understanding, I find myself nodding in agreement, eager to delve into this strategic approach that promises to offer clarity amidst the business's intricate workings.

Chloe continues, her fingers dancing across the keyboard as she pulls up a digital canvas, a canvas upon which WellQuest's journey toward progress is about to unfold.

"Let's identify your KPIs," she suggests, a twinkle in her eye hinting at the adventure ahead.

Under the dappled sunlight filtering through the leaves, Chloe scrolls through a document on the laptop. The soft clicks of the computer are interwoven with the melodies of chirping birds and the gentle rustle of leaves in the wind.

"First, let's talk about subscriber count and social media effectiveness", Chloe's eyes light up with a digital glow, mirroring the screen before us. "It's not just about the numbers," she emphasizes, "it's about creating a community, engaging with our audience, and fostering a sense of belonging."

The idea resonates with me deeply. Then, the dialogue turns to strategies for engaging content, storytelling, and genuine connections, weaving a tapestry of resonance beyond mere metrics.

After a few moments, Chloe changes the topic. "Next is customer satisfaction," she says. "Testimonials aren't just endorsements," she says with a smile. "They're reflections of lives transformed, of well-being restored" The scent of blossoms around us seems to underscore the heartwarming impact I've already had and the lives I will eventually touch. I smile, remembering the true reason behind WellQuest.

"And, let's not forget about financial health," Chloe adds. "Just like your garden, growth requires sustenance." Chloe's guidance on balancing revenue and expenses feel like the ebb and flow of nature itself, a dance of resources in harmony.

"What about employee productivity?" I add in, which sparks a discussion on team dynamics.

"It's like tending to your garden," Chloe muses, gesturing around us. "Each plant needs the right care, the right environment to thrive." The thought resonates as I think about how that can apply to Emily and Jack.

"Oh, and the last thing we need to keep in mind is the retention rate," Chloe adds. "It's not just about gaining clients," she says. "It's about building connections that withstand time."

With each topic discussed Chloe adds it to the list on her laptop. *Subscriber Count. Customer Satisfaction. Financial Health. Employee Productivity. Retention Rate.*

"Now that these are listed out," Chloe announces, "We can use these scorecards to track your progress in each of these areas. This way, you can monitor your success and make adjustments accordingly."

I scan the laptop screen, a smile forming on my face. "This is all great," I say. "Thank you so much."

Chloe returns my smile but then says, "Well, it doesn't just stop there. We also need employee scorecards."

So, Chloe and I dive into the task of crafting department scorecards for Jack and Emily. The soft breeze carries the scent of blooming flowers, infusing the process with a sense of purpose and renewal.

With Jack's scorecard, we embark on a journey into the financial realm of WellQuest. "Let's start with revenue growth," Chloe suggests, her fingers dancing across the keyboard. We discuss strategies to optimize income streams, exploring avenues for expansion while maintaining financial stability.

"Cost management," Chloe continues, and we delve into the intricacies of resource allocation and expense control, much like a gardener meticulously caring for a blossoming garden.

As we move through Jack's scorecard, topics like profitability and financial health come into focus. Chloe's guidance blends seamlessly with the tranquility of the garden, her words infusing the discussions with clarity and purpose. By the time we're finished, Jack's scorecard stands as a testament to the business's fiscal vitality, a roadmap to navigate the complex landscape of financial success.

Turning our attention to Emily's scorecard, a different energy fills the air. "Let's nurture the creative side," Chloe suggests with a smile.

Subscriber growth takes center stage, akin to planting seeds of engagement and watching them flourish. Social media engagement follows suit, reflecting the art of fostering genuine connections through captivating content.

As Chloe guides me through the creation of Emily's scorecard, we discuss metrics for content performance, a virtual garden of insights that reveals which content resonates with our audience.

"Audience interaction," Chloe adds, encouraging a dialogue between WellQuest and its community, much like the ongoing conversation between a garden and its caretaker.

As we wrap up, Emily's scorecard stands as a testament to the vibrant tapestry of WellQuest's online presence, a reflection of its ability to inspire, engage, and empower. With each department's scorecard complete, I find myself marveling at the convergence of structure and creativity, a harmonious blend that echoes the balance we seek in the garden and within the business.

And as the sun begins to set, casting a warm glow over our garden sanctuary, I realize that these scorecards are more than just documents; they're blueprints for growth, guides for nurturing both financial health and creative expression. With Chloe's guidance, we've not only crafted tools for progress but also cultivated a deeper understanding of the intricate dance between structure and innovation.

Gazing at the vibrant dashboard before me, a sense of accomplishment and empowerment washes over me. The scorecards, a culmination of collaboration and strategic planning, now stand as a visual representation of WellQuest's journey toward balance and growth.

The colors dance across the screen, each hue carrying a significance that transcends the digital realm. Green, a reassuring beacon of progress, symbolizes that we're on track, a testament to our hard work and commitment. Yellow, a gentle caution, reminds us to tread carefully and stay vigilant. And red, an urgent reminder to take action, prompts us to address challenges head-on and adapt to evolving circumstances.

Chloe's guidance in creating these scorecards has breathed life into mere data points. As I look at the intuitive design, I'm reminded of a well-tended garden, where the colors of the flowers convey their health and vitality, guiding the gardener's actions.

Promising myself to incorporate these scorecards into my daily routine, I recognize their power to steer WellQuest with precision and clarity. They're more than just tools; they're navigational aids on our journey to sustainable success. Just as a seasoned sailor reads the wind and the stars, I now have a compass to navigate the business's course with data-driven decision-making and adaptability.

Reflections

How do the elements of this chapter relate to your business?

Actions to Take

1 _____

2 _____

3 _____

CHAPTER 10

PRIDE ASIDE

Later that night, after Chloe had gone home, I get to work recording a video for the WellQuest Wellness Hub. Sitting in my office, the hum of the computer filling the air, I adjust the camera one last time. With a deep breath, I hit the record button, and the lens captures my earnest expression.

"Hello, everyone," I begin, my voice carrying a blend of warmth and confidence. I glance down at my notecards before continuing.

"In our fast-paced lives, it's easy to forget the simple act of breathing," I say, my words resonating with the experiences of countless individuals seeking respite from the demands of modern life. "Today, I am going to teach you some tips about deep-breathing exercises."

I demonstrate the techniques, guiding viewers through each inhale and exhale, the rhythm of my voice a soothing cadence.

As I wrap up the video, I can't help but smile, proud of what I've accomplished. With a few clicks, I save the recording, and a sense of satisfaction washes over me. I take a deep breath myself, a welcome respite after a day filled with productive conversations and innovative strategies.

Stepping out of my office, I'm met with a heartwarming scene. My mother and Emmy are on the rug engrossed in a simple game, their laughter blending harmoniously.

"Roll the ball, Emmy, just like this!" my mother encourages, her voice brimming with affection.

Emmy's bright eyes lock onto the colorful ball, and with a determined expression, she stretches out her tiny hand, attempting to mimic the movement. The ball wobbles and then rolls

a short distance before coming to a stop. A peal of giggles erupts from Emmy, a musical testament to her delight.

I lean against the door frame, my heart swelling with emotions I can't quite name. There's an ache of longing, a wish to be a part of these everyday moments.

My mother's eyes meet mine, and she offers a gentle smile. "Christine, come join us," she invites, patting the floor beside her.

I cross the room and settle beside them, my fingers brushing Emmy's soft curls.

"Hey there, little one," I coo, my voice a soothing melody. Emmy turns her attention to me, her eyes sparkling with curiosity.

"Roll the ball to Mama," my mother encourages.

With a mix of determination and innocence, Emmy gives the ball a little nudge, and it rolls clumsily in my direction. I catch it with a playful grin, marveling at the simplicity of this shared experience.

"Good job, Emmy! You're a pro," I exclaim, my words met with another round of giggles.

But then, Emmy's joyful laughter suddenly turns into heartrending sobs, throwing both my mother and me off balance. Without a moment's pause, I scoop her up into my arms, my heart racing with concern. "What's wrong, sweetheart?" I murmur softly, my voice trying to soothe her distress.

As I cradle her against my chest, Emmy's cries fill the room, a symphony of distress that threatens to unravel my patience. I glance at my mother, who reaches out her hand as if to offer help. I shake my head.

I'm sick of her always helping, I think to myself, *I want to calm down my own daughter.* I press a gentle kiss to Emmy's forehead, my lips brushing against her downy hair. "Shh, it's okay," I whisper, my fingers tracing soothing patterns on her back.

I start to pace around the living room, the rhythm of my steps an attempt to bring some semblance of comfort.

"You're safe, my love. Mama's here," I murmur, my voice a constant reassurance in the midst of her cries.

But the more I walk and murmur, the louder Emmy's cries seem to grow. My own frustration simmers beneath the surface, the helplessness gnawing at my resolve.

"Come on, Emmy," I mutter under my breath, my voice tinged with exasperation.

I try bouncing her gently, hoping the rhythmic motion might soothe her, but it only seems to intensify her cries. My frustration grows as her cries continue to pierce the air, a relentless reminder of my inability to ease her distress.

The weight of my pride and stubbornness hangs heavy in my thoughts. For so long, I had clung to the belief that I could handle it all on my own, that seeking help was a sign of weakness. But recent events have painted a different picture, one where seeking guidance and support is not only acceptable but incredibly effective.

As I sit here, pondering the undeniable success that Chloe's guidance has brought to my business, it's impossible to ignore the parallels in my personal life. My reluctance to reach out to my mother for advice feels almost childish in hindsight. After all, if seeking help can transform a chaotic business into a well-oiled machine, then surely it can bring some semblance of balance to my overwhelmed life as well.

The irony isn't lost on me. The same pride that kept me from seeking guidance in my business is now nudging me to acknowledge the wisdom of leaning on others, especially those who genuinely care about my well-being. It's a humbling realization, one that both stings and soothes, like a bitter medicine with a healing touch.

With a sigh, I make up my mind. The barriers I had erected around seeking help are crumbling, replaced by the understanding that growth comes not from stubbornly shouldering burdens alone, but from embracing the guidance and support that life offers. It's time to let go of my pride and let in the wisdom of those who have walked this path before me, starting with the woman who raised me.

I turn back to my mother, my heartbeat quickening with a mixture of vulnerability and anticipation. It's time to admit that I don't have all the answers. I can't do it all alone. Seeking guidance is not a sign of weakness, but a testament to my commitment to growth and balance.

With a determined exhale, I kneel down on the rug where my mother is sitting.

"Mom," I start hesitantly, my voice carrying a mixture of vulnerability and determination. "I need your help. Sometimes she just starts crying and I don't know what to do. I've tried everything, and it feels like nothing works."

My mother's eyes soften with understanding as she leans forward slightly. "It's not uncommon for babies to have moments like that, Christine. You went through the same thing when you were little."

I lean back in my chair, a mixture of surprise and realization washing over me. "Wait, really?"

She nods, her smile widening. "Yes. You used to get so fussy and would cry inconsolably. But there was one thing that always seemed to calm you down."

I lean in, curious and eager. "What was it?"

My mother's eyes twinkle with fond memories. "I used to sing you a lullaby, a simple song that seemed to have a magical effect on you. It was like your own personal off-switch for crying."

A small smile tugs at the corners of my lips as I imagine my mother soothing a young me with a song. "And do you remember the lullaby?"

She chuckles softly. "How could I forget? It was 'Twinkle, Twinkle, Little Star.' Every time you heard that song, you would gradually stop crying and just listen."

I take a moment to process her words, realizing the significance of what she's saying. "So, you're saying that I should try singing that to Emmy?"

My mother nods with certainty. "It's worth a shot. You might find that it has the same effect on her as it did on you."

I let out a breath I didn't realize I was holding, feeling a mix of relief and gratitude. "Thank you, Mom. I'll give it a try."

With my heart racing, I gently scoop Emmy up in my arms, cradling her close as I softly hum the familiar tune of "Twinkle, Twinkle, Little Star". Her cries begin to waver, replaced by a curious, wide-eyed gaze. Emboldened by the small progress, I gather my courage and start singing the words, my voice quivering slightly.

"Twinkle, twinkle, little star," I sing, my voice tentative but filled with a mother's determination. "How I wonder what you are..."

Emmy's cries start to quiet, her tiny fingers gripping onto the fabric of my shirt. With each word, her breath steadies, and her eyes begin to droop with drowsiness.

My mother watches the scene with a gentle smile, her eyes conveying pride and understanding.

"You're doing great, Christine," she whispers, her voice a soothing backdrop to my efforts.

"Up above the world so high..."

As I continue to sing, the room seems to settle into a tranquil cocoon, the only sounds are the soft melody and Emmy's gradually calming breaths. And then, almost miraculously, her cries cease altogether. She blinks sleepily at me, her tiny chest rising and falling rhythmically.

My heart swells with a mix of relief and gratitude as I look at my daughter, peaceful in my arms. I turn to my mother, who is beaming at us both.

"It worked," I whisper, my voice filled with awe.

My mother's smile deepens, her eyes glistening with a mixture of pride and love. She whispers back, "I knew it would."

But her words don't stop there. She leans in closer, her expression sincere. "And Christine, I want you to know how proud I am of you."

I'm taken aback by her words, my emotions a jumble of surprise and warmth. "Proud of me? For what?"

My mother's gaze softens as she speaks from the heart. "For everything you've done with your business, for your dedication and determination. Even though I didn't fully understand it at first, I see now how much you've accomplished."

Tears prick at the corners of my eyes as her words wash over me. My journey with WellQuest has been a rollercoaster, marked by challenges and triumphs. To hear my mother acknowledge the significance of my efforts is a validation I didn't know I needed.

"Thank you," I say softly, my voice trembling with emotion.

She reaches over and gently squeezes my hand. "You're making your own path, just like you are with Emmy. And I couldn't be prouder."

As I sit there, my daughter in my arms and my mother's support by my side, I realize that the journey of motherhood and entrepreneurship is paved with unexpected moments of connection and growth. With my mother's guidance, I've learned that seeking support and embracing change are not signs of weakness, but pathways to success.

Reflections

How do the elements of this chapter relate to your business?

Actions to Take

1 _____

2 _____

3 _____

CHAPTER 11

FIXING THE CLASHES

I step into the home office, a fresh cup of tea in hand. The soft morning light filters through the curtains, a sign of a fresh day ahead. Jack is focused on his own laptop, engrossed in the financial reports for WellQuest. Emily is nestled in a corner, her fingers dancing across the keyboard as she manages the social media content.

Today will be a great day, I think.

"Good morning, everyone," I greet, my voice infused with a blend of enthusiasm and determination.

"Morning," Jack responds with a nod, his fingers flying over the keyboard as he enters data.

Emily looks up from her screen and adjusts her glasses, her smile brightening the room. "Morning, Christine. Ready to tackle the day?"

I chuckle, a mixture of exhaustion and eagerness in my eyes. "As ready as I can be," I say.

Jack glances up from the laptop, his orange hair falling into his eyes. "Hey, Christine, do you have financial reports from last month?"

I nod and reach for a folder on my desk. "Right here. Let me print them out for you."

As I reach for them, Emily lets out a triumphant cheer. "Got another batch of responses for the social media campaign! People seem to be loving your deep breathing video."

"That's fantastic, Emily," I reply, a note of pride in my voice. "Keep up the great work."

Satisfied with my new employees, I grab my camera and yoga mat and carry them out to the backyard. Today, I'm determined to create a yoga video that centers around the "Downward-Facing Dog" pose. It's a fundamental pose, one that encapsulates the essence of grounding and stretching.

Satisfied with the progress of the day, I decide to shift gears and focus on a different task. I grab my camera and set it up in a corner of the room, creating a makeshift studio space. Today, I'm determined to create a yoga video that centers around the "Downward-Facing Dog" pose. It's a fundamental pose, one that encapsulates the essence of grounding and stretching.

"Alright, the camera's set up, and I'm ready to roll," I mutter to myself, adjusting the angle and checking the lighting.

With a calm demeanor, I position myself on the yoga mat, ensuring the camera captures my every movement.

"Hello, crew! Today, we are going to learn about the 'Downward-Facing Dog' pose," I say, smiling into the camera.

The soft sunlight and serene atmosphere of the yard contribute to the ambiance I'm trying to create. As I flow into the pose, my body responds gracefully, and I feel the tension in my muscles releasing.

"Starting with a deep breath in… and exhale, let your heels press into the ground."

I guide myself through each step, each transition, articulating the nuances of the pose for those who will follow along. My voice is steady and soothing, a gentle guide for anyone seeking a moment of tranquility. The flow is as much a meditation for me as it is an instructional video for others.

"As you lengthen through your spine, feel the stretch from your fingertips to your tailbone."

With each movement, I let go of the stress and demands of the day, embracing the serenity that yoga offers. My focus remains on the present, on the rhythm of my breath, and the alignment of my body. As I hold the pose, I feel a sense of balance and empowerment, a testament to the harmony I strive to bring to every aspect of my life.

"And gently come back down, finding your way to Child's Pose."

As the video recording comes to an end, I find myself in a deep state of relaxation. I've not only created content for WellQuest but also reconnected with the essence of wellness that I preach. With a contented smile, I turn off the camera, knowing that this video will contribute to the holistic journey of those who watch it.

My phone's insistent ringing pulls my attention away from the yoga mat and the peaceful atmosphere I've just created. I reach for it and glance at the caller ID, which reads "Brownsville Legal Associates". Curious and slightly apprehensive, I answer the call.

"Hello, you've reached WellQuest, Christine speaking," I say, my voice a mixture of curiosity and professionalism.

"Hi, Christine, this is Sarah Dawson from Brownsville Legal Associates. I hope I'm not catching you at a bad time," a friendly voice responds.

"Not at all, Sarah. What can I do for you?" I inquire, my curiosity growing.

Sarah explains the reason for her call: a necessary change in the timing of the upcoming talk I'm scheduled to have. As she goes over the details, I mentally juggle the adjustments that might be required on my end.

"We had an unforeseen scheduling conflict, and I apologize for the inconvenience. The new time we're proposing is tomorrow at 9 am. Would that work for you?" Sarah asks.

I take a moment to consider my calendar, making sure the change won't disrupt other commitments. "Yes, the new time works for me. Thank you for letting me know in advance."

"Great! I appreciate your understanding, Christine. We'll update our records accordingly. Is there anything else you need from us?" Sarah asks.

"No, that should be all. Thank you for reaching out and making the necessary arrangements," I reply, my gratitude evident in my tone.

With a polite exchange of farewells, we hang up. I take a deep breath and feel a sense of relief that the adjustment can be accommodated without much hassle.

I step back into the house, a sense of accomplishment from the completed yoga video still lingering in my thoughts. With a satisfied smile, I make my way to the home office to share the news with my new employees.

"Emily, guess what? I just finished recording the 'Downward-Facing Dog' video," I announce, my voice infused with a mix of pride and excitement.

Emily looks up from her computer, her expression shifting from concentration to surprise. "Wait, seriously? You finished it already?"

I nod, my smile widening. "Yes, I thought it was time to get that one done."

Her eyes widen, and there's something in her expression that makes me pause. "Are you sure, Christine? Because I actually posted a video for 'Downward-Facing Dog' last night."

I freeze, my heart skipping a beat. "What? Are you serious?"

Emily's eyes hold a mixture of surprise and concern. "Yes, I thought you wanted to get it out as soon as possible, so I went ahead and shot the footage last night and posted it on our social media"

Anger bubbles up within me, and I feel a mix of frustration and disbelief. "Emily, I can't believe you didn't check with me before posting it! We need to coordinate our efforts to avoid duplicating content."

Emily's face turns red, and she stammers, "I... I'm really sorry, Christine. I thought I was helping by getting it out there quickly."

I take a deep breath, trying to manage my frustration. "I appreciate your enthusiasm, Emily, but we need to communicate better about these things. Duplicating content can confuse our audience and make us look disorganized."

As I'm still trying to navigate the situation with Emily, Jack's voice breaks through the tension in the room. "Hey, Christine, just got off the phone with someone from Brownsville Elementary. They want you to do a presentation tomorrow at 10am. Your schedule was free so I penciled them in."

What? I think, my heart sinking as I process the information.

My eyebrows furrow as I process the information. "Tomorrow? But I rescheduled the talk at the law firm for the same time."

Jack's expression changes from neutral to cautious as he notices my growing frustration. "I thought it would be a good opportunity, and they seemed really eager. I didn't want to miss out."

My anger starts to simmer as I respond, my voice clipped. "Jack, you can't just schedule things without running them by me first. We need to coordinate and make sure our commitments align."

He looks genuinely apologetic, which only adds to my annoyance. "I'm sorry, Christine. I thought I was helping."

I take a deep breath, reminding myself to stay composed. "I appreciate your initiative, but we must communicate and make decisions together. Now, I have to figure out how to handle two commitments at the same time."

Frustration churns within me, and I can feel the tension escalating. Without a word, I snatch my laptop and storm outside, needing the distance from both Emily and Jack. I settle into a chair in the garden, the soft breeze offering a fleeting sense of calm amid the chaos.

How can they be so incapable? I fume. *How could they make such pointless mistakes?*

Opening my laptop, I take a few deep breaths to steady myself. I review the footage I had diligently recorded for the Downward-Facing Dog video, my irritation growing as I remember Emily's claim about the duplicate post. I pause, my fingers hovering over the keyboard, as I decide to save my own footage for later, ensuring it won't be reposted.

It's a small act of control in a situation that feels out of control. As I type away, I can't shake the frustration that's settled in my chest.

Next task, I think, pulling out my phone.

I take a deep breath, my fingers tapping the numbers to call the law firm. Sarah's voice greets me on the other end, and I quickly explain the situation, my frustration making my words sharper than intended.

"I need to reschedule the talk we had planned for tomorrow. There's been a mix-up with my schedule."

Sarah sounds genuinely confused, her tone reflecting the unexpected nature of my call. "Oh, I see. Is everything okay?"

I cringe. I hate being unprofessional but I need to fix the mistake that Jack made. I sigh, willing myself to remain composed.

"There's another presentation I need to handle tomorrow," I say slowly, "an unexpected one. I can't be in two places at once."

There's a moment of silence on her end, and I can almost sense her processing the situation. "Alright, Christine. It's a bit unusual, but we can wait until next week. Just let us know when you're available."

"Thank you, Sarah. I appreciate your understanding," I reply.

I end the call with a mixture of relief and frustration, my emotions mingling like a storm within me. It's frustrating to find myself in a situation where I have to untangle the knots created by miscommunication. The weight of it all settles on my shoulders.

A sense of annoyance tugs at me as I contemplate the need to fix these issues, to step in and rectify the situations that have arisen. I have worked hard to establish a professional image for WellQuest, and these bumps in the road are making me feel like I'm slipping on my own path.

As my frustration simmers, I realize I need an outlet to release the pent-up energy swirling within me. With a sense of determination, I slip on my running shoes and head out the backyard gate, craving the rhythmic pounding of my feet on the pavement to match the rhythm of my racing thoughts.

The world outside feels different, open, unburdened. Each step propels me forward, pushing the concerns and stresses of the day to the back of my mind. The air is crisp, and with every inhale and exhale, I feel a bit of the tension easing.

As I round a corner, lost in the rhythm of my run, a familiar figure catches my eye. It's Lily, speed-walking down the sidewalk. Her vibrant red hair is adorned with streaks of bold purple, a reflection of her free spirit.

I slow down and approach her with a warm smile. "Hey, Lily! Fancy meeting you here," I say in a joking tone.

Lily grins back, her eyes sparkling with a mix of surprise and delight. "Christine! Hey, I'm surprised to see you out running in the middle of the day. Aren't your new employees in your office?"

I sigh, wanting to keep things light. "I'm just taking a little break, I say. Running is my way of clearing my head."

Lily places a hand on her baby bump, her pace slowing a bit. "Trust me, I get it. This little one has me moving more than I thought I would!"

We fall into step together, our strides matching as we walk. We walk in silence for a little while, the rhythmic motion of our steps the only sound.

After a minute, Lily turns to me. "So, what's going on now?" she asks.

I roll my eyes. "What makes you think something's going on?"

"I know you, Christine!" she says, linking her arm in the crook of my elbow. "Come on now, tell me."

She always sees right through me, I think.

"Okay, fine," I say with a sigh. "It's just that, so far, things with Emily and Jack are rough." I pull my arm from hers and turn to face her. "You wouldn't believe the mistakes they made today. It's like something out of a sitcom!"

She chuckles. "Oh, come on, it can't be that bad," she said.

"I mean it!" I say with conviction. "I feel like I'm the only one holding everything together. Sure, I'm grateful to have Emily and Jack on board, but sometimes it feels like I have to constantly fix things or redo their work."

Lily listens attentively, her expression thoughtful. "You know, one thing that's helped me in my job at the school is setting up clear communication channels. It might be helpful for you to do the same."

I raise an eyebrow, intrigued by her suggestion. "What do you mean?"

Lily explains, "Well, imagine if you had regular check-ins with your team, where you discuss priorities, share progress, and address any challenges. Like a staff meeting. This way, you can all be on the same page and avoid misunderstandings."

I consider her words, realizing that she might be onto something. "That does make sense. It could prevent a lot of the issues that have been cropping up."

Lily nods, her expression encouraging. "Exactly. And remember, you don't have to do everything yourself. Delegating is important, but so is giving your team the tools and guidance they need to succeed."

Her advice strikes a chord with me, resonating as a solution to many of the problems I've been grappling with. "You're right, Lily. I need to create a better system for communication and collaboration. It'll not only ease my burden but also empower my team to excel."

Lily smiles, her support evident. "I believe in you, Christine. You've already come so far with WellQuest. Just remember that asking for help and setting up effective systems are signs of a strong leader."

As we continue walking, I'm filled with a renewed sense of purpose. Lily's words have given me a clear direction to navigate the challenges ahead. And amidst the support of a friend and the gentle rhythm of our footsteps, I'm reminded that even in the midst of chaos, solutions are waiting to be uncovered.

Reflections

How do the elements of this chapter relate to your business?

Actions to Take

1 _____

2 _____

3 _____

CHAPTER 12

SMOOTH SAILING

In the kitchen, the scent of vanilla and butter fills the air as I gather the ingredients for a batch of chocolate chip cookies.

As work, I reflect on Lily's suggestion for a staff meeting and a surge of gratitude washes over me. It's a simple yet powerful idea that holds the potential to bridge the communication gaps and foster a stronger team dynamic. I check the clock, knowing that my employees will arrive shortly. I'm excited to meet with them, go over things, and get everyone on the same page.

I measure flour, sugar, and chocolate chips with a sense of purpose. I crack eggs, their yolks a vibrant golden hue, and slowly incorporate them into the mixture.

But, while I mix, my heart weighs heavy with remorse for my outburst the other day. Yelling at my employees wasn't the leader I strive to be.

I want to make things right, I think to myself, *these cookies will be the first step.*

With the dough ready, I preheat the oven, the soft hum of the appliance punctuating the silence. With the cookies arranged in neat rows, I slide the baking sheet into the oven, watching through the glass door as they transform into golden perfection.

This small gesture to show my appreciation and to mend the fractures that my frustration had caused. Just as the ingredients come together to create something delightful, I hope this act of goodwill will contribute to a more harmonious atmosphere within WellQuest.

The minutes tick by, the aroma growing richer, until finally, the timer dings. Carefully, I remove the cookies from the oven, the warmth seeping through my oven mitts. As the cookies cool on a wire rack, I set about arranging them on a plate, their textures inviting and their aroma irresistible.

They'll love this, I think.

With a satisfied smile, I carry the plate into the home office, where the meeting is set to take place. The cookies stand as a peace offering, a gesture to symbolize our shared journey towards better communication and collaboration. As I step back and take in the scene, I feel a sense of hope. This small act, this batch of cookies, is a testament to the power of unity, and I'm determined to make this staff meeting a step towards a more harmonious and productive future.

As Emily and Jack step into the home office, their presence punctuates the air with a mix of anticipation and nervousness. The aroma of freshly baked cookies lingers, a tangible reminder of the effort I've put into creating a welcoming environment.

"Hey, everyone," I greet with a genuine smile, my voice carrying a note of warmth and sincerity.

"Hey, Christine," Emily responds, twisting her long blond hair in her hands in a nervous way.

Jack nods in acknowledgment, a subtle gesture that carries a world of unspoken understanding.

Before the conversation even begins, I take a deep breath, a silent acknowledgment of the past events that led us to this moment. The honesty in my voice reflects my intent as I address them.

"I want to start by saying that I'm sorry for how things unfolded yesterday. I realize that communication could have been better, and I take full responsibility for that."

Emily's eyes meet mine, her response gentle yet genuine. "Thank you for acknowledging that, Christine. We appreciate it."

Jack chimes in, his voice is measured and thoughtful. "It's important that we all learn from these situations. Communication goes both ways, and we should have made sure to discuss any changes in plans with you."

I feel a sense of relief and gratitude wash over me as their understanding and acceptance fill the room. It's a small yet significant step towards the kind of open and collaborative dynamic we're working to build within the team.

"I promise that moving forward, we'll make an effort to communicate more effectively and ensure that decisions are made collectively," I assure them, my commitment palpable in every word.

Emily nods in agreement, her smile a reflection of our shared dedication to improvement. "Sounds like a plan."

Jack's response carries a sense of optimism. "Absolutely. Let's turn this into an opportunity to grow and work together even better."

With their forgiveness and determination echoing in the room, I feel a renewed sense of purpose and unity. The cookies on the table, once a symbol of peace, now serve as a reminder of our capacity to learn and evolve as a team. As we gather around, ready to embark on the staff meeting, I'm filled with the hope that this open dialogue will pave the way for a stronger, more harmonious WellQuest.

"Alright," I begin, settling into my seat. "Let's get down to business. From now on, I want us to have these weekly meetings, a chance to communicate, share progress, and ensure we're all on the same page."

Emily, her gaze focused and determined, nods in agreement. "Absolutely, Christine. This will help us stay aligned and tackle challenges together." She reaches for a cookie and takes a bite.

Jack, his usual calm demeanor unchanged, adds, "It's a great idea. Having a designated time to discuss everything will prevent any confusion down the line."

Grabbing a cookie, I continue, "In addition to these meetings, we'll implement monthly reviews to address concerns and discuss personal growth within your roles."

Emily's eyes light up with enthusiasm as she interjects, "That sounds fantastic. It's an opportunity to receive feedback and also set goals."

"And, for a broader view," I say, "we'll have quarterly sprint planning sessions to set targets and ensure our goals align with WellQuest's vision." Jack leans back, nodding in approval. "That'll keep us focused on the bigger picture while also allowing us to adjust as needed."

I take a bite of the cookie, savoring the sweetness. I usually stay away from unhealthy food, I have to practice what I preach, but I remember what Lily said. *Indulge a little.* I figure if I made these for my team, I deserve one too.

Returning my focus to my employees, I say, "I wanted to introduce something new that I think will really help us stay on track and aligned. You've probably noticed the scorecards on the table. These are going to be a central part of our communication moving forward."

Emily's curiosity sparks, and she leans in for a closer look. "Scorecards?"

I nod, taking a moment to explain. "Yes, scorecards. They're visual representations of our key performance indicators or KPIs. Basically, they're going to help us track our progress and identify areas where we can improve."

Jack seems intrigued, his analytical mind already working. "So, these will give us a clear picture of how we're doing across different aspects of the business?" He idly reaches for a cookie as well.

"Exactly," I confirm with a smile. "For instance, we'll have sections like Subscriber Count and Social Media Effectiveness, Customer Satisfaction, Financial Health, Employee Productivity, and Retention Rate. These scorecards will help us visualize our progress and give us a baseline for making data-driven decisions."

Emily nods, absorbing the information. She takes a bite of the cookie before saying, "It sounds like a great way to stay focused and accountable."

"Absolutely," I agree. "And that's not all. Alongside these weekly meetings, we'll have monthly reviews where we can dig deeper into our progress and discuss any challenges or opportunities. And every quarter, we'll hold sprint planning sessions to set goals and strategies for the upcoming months."

Jack leans back, clearly impressed. "It sounds like a comprehensive system that will keep us aligned and proactive."

"That's the goal," I say with satisfaction. "I believe that with these scorecards and regular meetings, we'll be able to streamline our efforts and make WellQuest even stronger."

As we continue our conversation, munching on the cookies I had baked as a small gesture of unity, I'm struck by the sense of purpose that fills the room. These scorecards are more than just numbers on paper; they're a reflection of our commitment to each other and to the vision we share. As we embrace this new chapter of communication and collaboration, I can't help but feel a renewed sense of optimism for what lies ahead.

As the productive meeting wraps up and my staff members leave, a familiar cry echoes through the house. Emmy's tears tug at my heartstrings, and I quickly make my way to her.

I scoop her up in my arms, gently swaying.

"It's okay, baby," I whisper, trying to calm her. But, she doesn't stop crying. "Come on, now," I think, frustration growing.

But then, I remember what my mother taught me. I clear my throat and begin to sing, "Twinkle, twinkle, little star…"

As I continue to hum the melody, Emmy's tiny body relaxes against mine, her soft sobs gradually fading away. It's a delicate dance, a dance of reassurance and comfort, and I can feel the tension in her little frame melting as the soothing notes wrap around us. I press my cheek against her velvety hair, my heartbeat syncing with the rhythm of the song.

"That's it, my sweet Emmy. Mama's got you," I coo.

And just like that, the storm of tears subsides, replaced by the steady rise and fall of Emmy's breathing. As her eyelids grow heavy, I'm reminded of the power of presence, the simple act of being there for her in this moment of need. It's a connection that transcends words, a bond that grows stronger with each hummed note.

Amidst the relief, a shadow of doubt creeps in.

What if this won't last?

I can't help but worry that the calm won't last and that the challenges and uncertainties of balancing motherhood and entrepreneurship will return. It's a fear that lingers, a constant reminder that the road ahead won't always be smooth sailing.

Reflections

How do the elements of this chapter relate to your business?

Actions to Take

1 _____

2 _____

3 _____

CHAPTER 13

PLANNING AHEAD

In the serene embrace of the garden, I find myself amid the vibrant blooms and flourishing greens. Each stroke of my hands as I nurture the soil mirrors the care and attention I've invested in WellQuest. It's a moment of contentment, witnessing nature's growth intertwined with my business's progress.

A sense of achievement swells within me as I water the plants, reminiscing about the recent victories we've achieved as a team. The synchronized efforts, innovative ideas, and steady strides toward our goals have been invigorating. Yet, a niggling doubt shadows my elation.

What if this won't last?

As the sun's rays dance through the leaves, I contemplate the ebb and flow of success. The fear of unforeseen challenges creeping in is undeniable. Like the changing weather, business cycles are bound to shift. It's a realization that tempers my optimism with a dose of caution.

Suddenly, I hear footsteps behind me. I stand up to see Chloe, who had let herself in through my backyard gate. Her sleek, white hair blows in the breeze as she approaches me. I straighten up, wiping my hands on my apron, and offer her a grateful smile.

"Chloe, I can't thank you enough for coming on such short notice," I say.

"Of course, Christine. I'm here to support you in any way I can," Chloe says as she settles onto a nearby bench. "What's on your mind?"

I exhale slowly, the weight of my worries lifting a fraction as I voice the nagging fear that's been playing on repeat in my mind.

"It's just... Chloe, I'm scared that I won't be able to sustain this progress, that everything we've worked so hard for will unravel. Balancing WellQuest and being a mother – it's a constant tightrope walk, and I fear I'll falter." With a sigh, I sit next to her on the bench.

Chloe's gaze is steady, her empathy palpable. She leans closer as if bridging the emotional distance between us.

"Christine, what you're feeling is completely natural. Entrepreneurship and motherhood are both demanding roles, and it's okay to have moments of doubt. But remember, you've already shown incredible resilience and determination. You've built WellQuest from the ground up while nurturing a precious bond with Emmy. That's no small feat."

Her words are a gentle reminder, a lifeline to anchor me in reality. I take a deep breath, finding a glimmer of reassurance in her understanding.

"I just want to be the best I can be for Emmy and Ethan. And especially for WellQuest. I want to maintain this momentum without compromising either."

Chloe's eyes hold a depth of understanding, a reflection of the challenges she's witnessed me face.

"Christine, progress isn't always a straight line. There will be bumps along the way, and moments of uncertainty. But what truly matters is your commitment to growth, and your willingness to adapt and seek help when needed. You've already demonstrated that with Emily and Jack, and with your dedication to creating a balanced structure for WellQuest."

As her words sink in, a sense of relief washes over me, washing away the doubts that had taken root.

After a moment she smiles, the kind that suggests a well-thought-out idea.

"What if we create a comprehensive three-year plan for the company?" she says. "A roadmap that outlines not just the growth strategies, but also potential challenges and solutions."

Her words hang in the air, and I consider her proposition.

A three-year plan, I think.

It's an intriguing notion, one that could potentially provide the stability I long for. "Tell me more, Chloe," I say.

With a thoughtful expression, Chloe elaborates, "Having a structured plan can help alleviate your fears of unpredictability. We'll identify key milestones, growth targets, and allocate resources accordingly. It will serve as a guide, giving us a sense of direction even during uncertain times."

I take a moment to absorb her words. The idea resonates with me, offering a sense of clarity that I've been seeking. "You think it will truly help?" I ask.

Chloe's eyes meet mine, earnest and sincere. "Absolutely. It's about proactive preparation and building resilience. Just like a garden needs regular tending and care, a business thrives when it's nurtured with foresight and strategy."

Her analogy strikes a chord, and a renewed determination ignites within me. "Alright, Chloe. Let's do it. Let's create that three-year plan for WellQuest."

With our conversation in the garden lingering in the air like a promise, Chloe and I make our way back inside. There's a sense of purpose that accompanies us, a shared determination to shape the future of WellQuest in a more deliberate manner. As we step into the cozy confines of the house, I offer Chloe a warm smile.

"Would you like some tea?" I ask, heading towards the kitchen.

Chloe's appreciative nod fuels my enthusiasm, and I set about preparing the tea with a sense of care. The kettle's soft hum and the aroma of the brewing tea create a soothing backdrop, as if the universe itself is conspiring to make this moment a tranquil one. In no time, the cups are ready, steaming tendrils rising from them.

I return to the home office, cups in hand, and Chloe settles in comfortably in front of the computer. The soft glow of the screen illuminates her thoughtful expression. I hand her a cup of tea and take a seat beside her.

"Thank you for suggesting this, Chloe," I say, feeling a blend of gratitude and anticipation.

Chloe's smile is both reassuring and eager. "I truly believe it's a step in the right direction, Christine. Our shared vision and commitment will shape this plan into something remarkable."

We sip our tea and begin discussing the structure of the three-year plan. Soon, the screen before us transforms into a canvas of possibilities as we delve into the creation of WellQuest's three-year plan. With each strategic goal and set of objectives, I feel a renewed sense of purpose and excitement building within me.

"Okay, year 1," I begin, my fingers dancing across the keyboard as I type out the first strategic goal. "Expand WellQuest's client base by 30% in the first year."

Chloe nods in agreement, her focused expression mirroring my own enthusiasm. "That's a solid goal. Let's break it down into quarterly sprints to keep us on track."

I eagerly type out the objectives under Year 1, our collective thoughts flowing seamlessly. "Launch targeted marketing campaigns, offer special promotions, enhance the website…"

Chloe interjects, her voice brimming with ideas. "And for each quarter, we can develop strategies, launch campaigns, analyze data, and evaluate results."

As we move on to Year 2, Chloe's insight shines once again. "Strengthen client engagement and retention. We can conduct surveys, enhance the assessment process, and implement regular check-ins."

I find myself nodding in agreement, my excitement growing as I envision the impact of these improvements. "Exactly. The quarterly sprints will allow us to gather feedback, revamp our processes, and continuously adapt to our clients' needs."

Finally, we arrive at Year 3, and Chloe's creativity takes center stage. "Introduce innovative wellness workshops and events. Collaborate with experts, organize events, and leverage social media."

I can't help but smile as I type, feeling the anticipation of what this could mean for WellQuest's future. "These workshops and events could truly set us apart and provide valuable experiences for our clients."

As we finalize the plan, Chloe and I share a satisfied look. The screen now displays a roadmap of growth, innovation, and connection. Our collaboration has brought this vision to life, and I can't help but feel a deep sense of gratitude for Chloe's guidance and support.

"We've done it, Christine," Chloe says with a smile. "This plan will guide you towards incredible growth and success."

I nod, feeling a blend of pride and determination. "And with your expertise and partnership, I know we can make it happen. Let's bring WellQuest to new heights."

Reflections

How do the elements of this chapter relate to your business?

Actions to Take

1 _____

2 _____

3 _____

CHAPTER 14

A PLEASANT PURPOSE

Reflections

How do the elements of this chapter relate to your business?

Actions to Take

1 _____

2 _____

3 _____

RESOURCES

Find us at https://www.DynamoGuru.com.

We offer a monthly DynamoGuru challenge. For information, go to https://www.DynamoGuru.com/challenge.

We also offer a membership where you can collaborate with other experts and get training to build your business. For information, go to https://www.DynamoGuru.com/membership

Also, check out https://www.BusinessResultsSystems.com

We offer a monthly Arrival Strategy challenge. For information, go to https://www.BusinessResultsSystems.com/challenge or https://www.ArrivalStrategy.com/challenge

We also offer a membership where you can collaborate with other business owners and get training to build your business. For information, go to https://www.BusinessResultsSystems.com/membership or https://www.ArrivalStrategy.com/membership

We offer training, group coaching, private coaching, and done-for-you services.

Find Business Results Systems on YouTube, Instagram, Facebook

Find Arrival Strategy on YouTube, Instagram, Facebook

Milton Keynes UK
Ingram Content Group UK Ltd.
UKHW030251190324
439698UK00015B/1058